17/8/24 £1

GCSE BIOLOGY *for* CCEA

REVISION BOOK

James Napier

GW00643754

HODDER EDUCATION
AN HACHETTE UK COMPANY

The Publishers would like to thank the following for permission to reproduce copyright material:

Photo p.49 © George McCarthy/CORBIS

Acknowledgements The Publishers are grateful to CCEA for their kind permission to reproduce past examination questions.

Orders: please contact Bookpoint Ltd, 130 Milton Park, Abingdon, Oxon OX14 4SB. Telephone: (44) 01235 827720. Fax: (44) 01235 400454. Lines are open 9.00–5.00, Monday to Saturday, with a 24-hour message answering service. Visit our website at www.hoddereducation.co.uk

First published in 2007 by Hodder Education, an Hachette UK company,
338 Euston Road
London NW1 3BH

Impression number 5
Year 2011 2010

Cover photo John Mitchell/Science Photo Library
Illustrations by Barking Dog Art
Typeset in Century ITC Light 11 on 13 point by Tech-Set Ltd, Gateshead, Tyne and Wear

Printed in Great Britain by the MPG Books Group, Bodmin

A catalogue record for this title is available from the British Library

ISBN: 978 0340 94055 6

Contents

Introduction

The purpose of this revision book is to help you fulfil your potential when you take GCSE Biology or the Biology component of Double Award Science (Modular or Non-modular) examinations.

The book outlines key biological facts and explains the underlying concepts in an approachable style. Particular attention is paid to topics and types of questions that have traditionally caused most difficulty.

As well as helping with knowledge and understanding, the book gives useful guidance in examination technique in the form of Examiner's notes. The notes highlight common misconceptions and mistakes made by students during examinations. They also explain how to use the correct terms and critical words to maximise your marks.

Using a carefully planned revision strategy which incorporates the reinforcement of core knowledge and essential understanding, this book will enable you to achieve your very best, whether you are striving to obtain an A or A* grade or whether you are hoping to achieve a grade C.

Format of the book

The chapters in the book are arranged in a similar order to its companion text, *GCSE Biology for CCEA*, although some of the individual chapters in that book are combined in this book.

In each chapter the most important points in each topic are explained and understanding is built up through the use of questions and typical answers. The questions in the book tend to be the longer questions worth 2–5 marks as opposed to the more straightforward one-word or 1-mark questions. At the end of a chapter there are past examination questions (without answers) that can be used for homework. Answers to the examination questions can be found within the text of this book.

- Parts of the book that are only applicable to students taking Double Award (Higher) are clearly identified by a **grey stripe** down the right-hand edge.
- Parts relevant only to GCSE Biology are identified by a **dotted stripe**.
- Parts required only for Biology (Higher) have a solid **black stripe**.

Some helpful hints

Before we have a look at some of the course content it is worth noting that many students fail to maximise their performance through misreading questions or not focusing answers sufficiently in terms of the question. Remember examiners can only mark what they see in the paper in front of them, not what they think you meant to write!

The words in the following table are often used in examination papers and it is important that you know exactly what each of them means. The words are often called 'command' words – they tell you what to do.

'Command' word	What you need to do
give/name/state	write down a short answer – possibly only one word – no explanation is needed
complete	answer in the spaces that have been provided – sometimes in boxes on diagrams or on answer lines at the end of the question or in gaps in a written paragraph
list	write a series of short answers – the word 'list' suggests there is more than one possible answer
describe	give a detailed account
explain	include an explanation of why or how
compare	describe the similarities and/or differences in the information
use the information in the diagram/paragraph, etc.	use only the information provided in the question in your answer
suggest/predict	although you are not expected to know the answer, you should be able to deduce or estimate it, either from information provided or from your knowledge

Sometimes two or more of these terms can be used together in the one question. For example, many questions start with 'Describe and explain ...'. These questions are almost always worth at least 2 marks: 1 mark for describing and at least 1 for the explanation. You will see many examples of this type of question in this book.

It is also important to recognise that if a question is worth 4 marks then you will usually need to make four separate points in your answer to gain full marks.

You may think that these comments simply state the obvious. However, it is amazing how many candidates are caught out by not following the rules!

Take the following example. This question was asked in Summer 2006.

Question

1 Name the **two** processes shown in the diagram. *[2]*

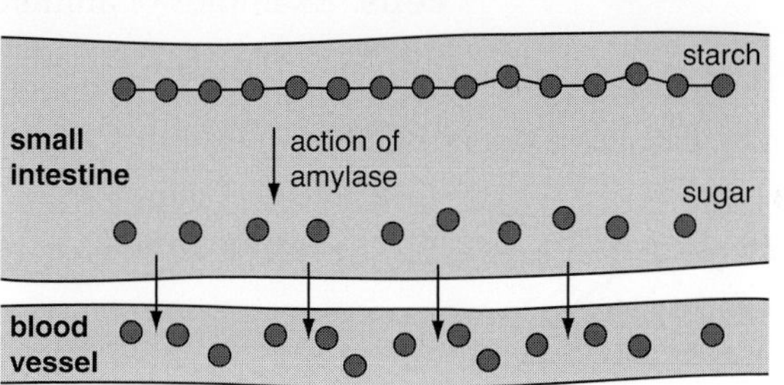
starch
small intestine
action of amylase
sugar
blood vessel

You probably can quickly work out that the diagram shows two important stages that take place in the digestive system. The diagram shows both the breakdown of food (digestion) and the passing of the breakdown products from the gut to the blood (absorption). As you can see, the question asks the candidate to **name** the **processes**. The answer is: **digestion** and **absorption** (although diffusion is allowed in place of absorption).

Would it surprise you to find out that many candidates did not name the processes but instead **described** what was taking place! Descriptions of the process without naming the processes gained no marks. This is an excellent example of how misinterpreting the question can cost marks – often all the marks for the question. It is also highly likely that many of the candidates who lost marks in this question knew what the processes were – they just failed to interpret the command word **name** in the question correctly.

This example summarises the rationale behind producing this book. It forms an invaluable tool for students who intend doing everything they can to obtain as many marks and therefore as high a grade as possible.

1

Cells and living organisms

Cells

Living organisms are made up of microscopic units called **cells**. Examples of animal and plant cells are shown in Figure 1.1.

Figure 1.1 An animal cell and a plant cell

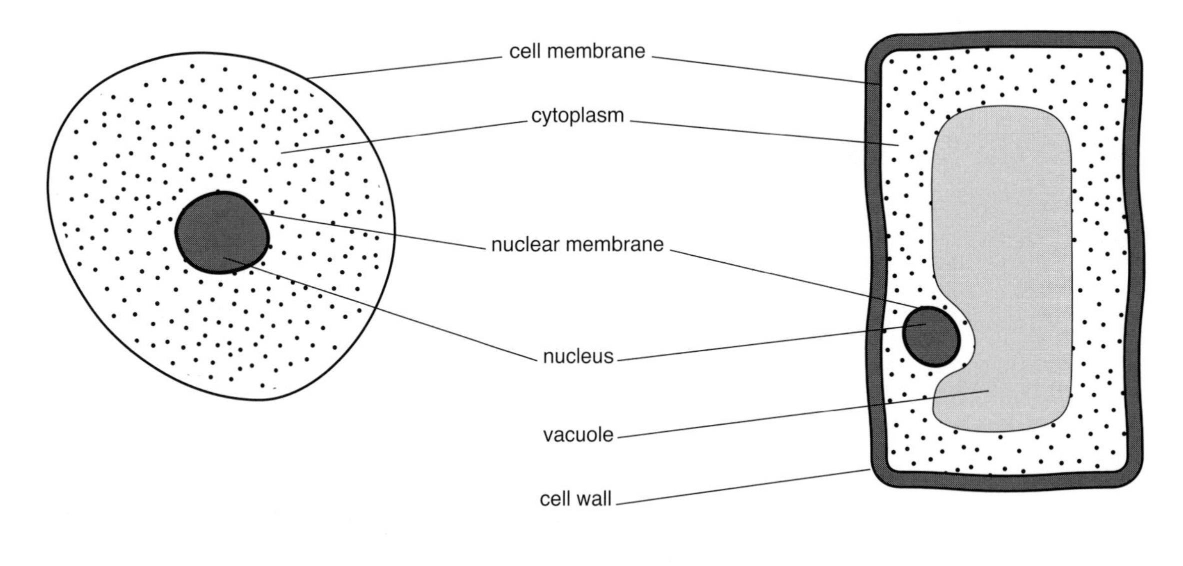

cell membrane
cytoplasm
nuclear membrane
nucleus
vacuole
cell wall
animal cell
plant cell

The functions and locations of the different parts of the cell are summarised in Table 1.1.

Table 1.1 The functions and locations of different parts of the cell

Structure	Function	Animal cell	Plant cell
cell membrane	forms a boundary to the cell and controls what enters and leaves the cell (partially permeable)	✓	✓
cytoplasm	main part of cell; chemical reactions occur here	✓	✓
nucleus	control centre of the cell; contains genetic information (in chromosomes)	✓	✓
vacuole	contains cell sap and gives the plant support through turgor	–	✓
cell wall	made of cellulose; it is a rigid structure that provides support	–	✓
chloroplast (found in green leaves)	contains chlorophyll to trap light during photosynthesis	–	✓
nuclear membrane	boundary of nucleus	✓	✓

Observing cells using a microscope

Figure 1.2 A light microscope and how it works

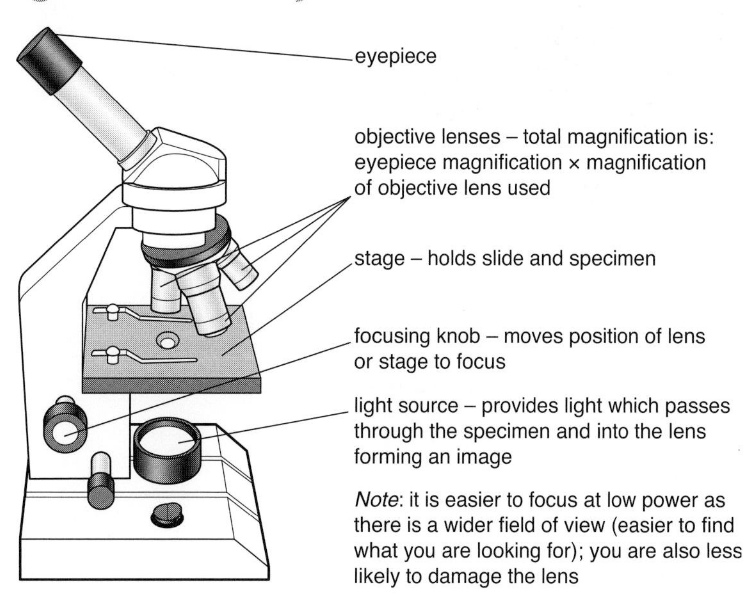
eyepiece
objective lenses – total magnification is: eyepiece magnification × magnification of objective lens used
stage – holds slide and specimen
focusing knob – moves position of lens or stage to focus
light source – provides light which passes through the specimen and into the lens forming an image
Note: it is easier to focus at low power as there is a wider field of view (easier to find what you are looking for); you are also less likely to damage the lens

Observing onion cells

1. Peel a small piece of onion epidermis from the inside of an onion. Make sure it is a thin, transparent layer (the layer of cells needs to be thin to allow light from the light source to pass through).
2. Using a pair of forceps place the onion epidermis evenly on a microscope slide.

3 Add water using a drop pipette to the onion epidermis to stop it drying out. (Or you could add a couple of drops of iodine to stain the onion cell, making parts such as the nucleus more obvious. You should wear safety goggles to do this.)
4 Carefully lower a cover slide over the layer of onion using a pointed needle (it is better to lower the cover slide one end first as this will avoid trapping air bubbles which are seen as thick black circles under the microscope). The cover slide protects the lens and stops the cells from drying out.
5 View your slide by placing it on the stage of the microscope and focusing at low power.
6 If greater magnification is needed switch to high power and re-focus.

Specialised cells

As well as looking at onion cells you have probably also observed some simple animal cells such as cheek cells. However, there are many cells (both plant and animal) that are **specialised** for specific purposes. The ones you need to know about are shown in Figure 1.3.

Figure 1.3 Specialised cells

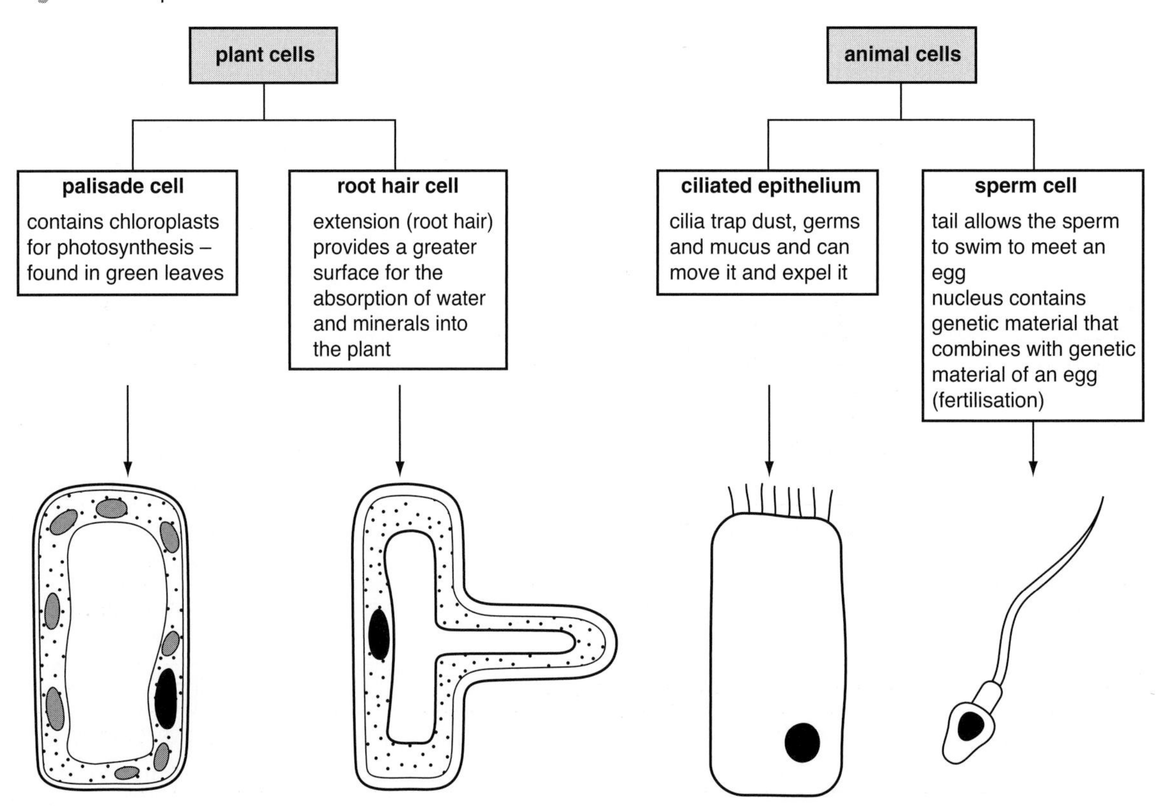
plant cells
palisade cell
contains chloroplasts for photosynthesis – found in green leaves
root hair cell
extension (root hair) provides a greater surface for the absorption of water and minerals into the plant
animal cells
ciliated epithelium
cilia trap dust, germs and mucus and can move it and expel it
sperm cell
tail allows the sperm to swim to meet an egg
nucleus contains genetic material that combines with genetic material of an egg (fertilisation)

Question

1 Copy and complete the table.

Name of cell	Function	Feature that adapts cell to its function
root hair cell		
	photosynthesis	
		tail for swimming

[3]

Typical answer

Name of cell	Function	Feature that adapts cell to its function
root hair cell	*absorption of water, minerals*	*extension to cell*
palisade cell	photosynthesis	*presence of chloroplasts*
sperm cell	*fertilisation*	tail for swimming

[3]

Tissues, organs and organ systems

Similar cells grouped together are referred to as a **tissue**. For example we have skin tissue and muscle tissue. An **organ** is a structure that is made up of several types of tissue that carries out a particular function. For example the heart is an organ that contains muscle and nervous tissue. Organs that operate together to carry out a particular function or functions are grouped together as **organ systems** as shown in Table 1.2.

Table 1.2 The organ systems and their functions

Organ system	Function	Main organs
digestive	breaking down of large molecules into simple, soluble molecules that are absorbed into the blood	stomach, small intestine
respiratory	supplying the body with oxygen and removing carbon dioxide from the body	lungs, diaphragm
skeletal	support, movement and protection	backbone, ribs, skull
circulatory	transport of materials, defence against disease and maintaining body temperature	heart, arteries
excretory	removal of toxic waste from the body	kidneys, bladder
reproductive	production of young	testes, ovaries, uterus
nervous	responding to stimuli and coordinating responses	brain, spinal cord

There are fewer organs in plants and they are not arranged in organ systems. The organs in plants and their functions are:

- **root:** absorbs water and mineral salts, usually also provides anchorage
- **stem:** supports plant and transports water and food in veins
- **leaf:** photosynthesis
- **flower:** reproduction.

Life processes – the characteristics of living things

All living organisms carry out the **life processes** shown in Figure 1.4.

Figure 1.4 Life processes carried out by all living organisms

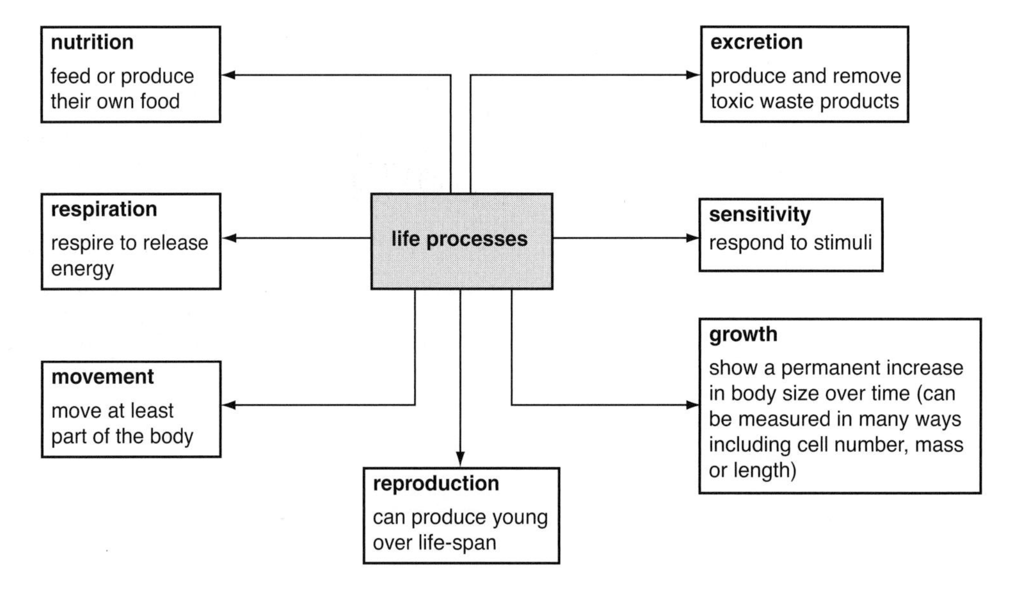
life processes
nutrition
feed or produce their own food
respiration
respire to release energy
movement
move at least part of the body
reproduction
can produce young over life-span
excretion
produce and remove toxic waste products
sensitivity
respond to stimuli
growth
show a permanent increase in body size over time (can be measured in many ways including cell number, mass or length)

Exam question

1 a The diagram shows a microscope.

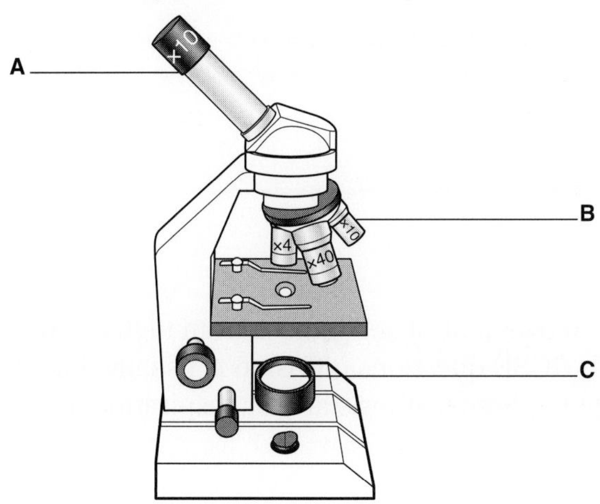
A
x10
B
x4
x40
x10
C

i Name parts A, B and C. *[3]*

ii Calculate the magnification being used. **Show your working**. *[2]*

You are provided with a thin strip of onion tissue.

iii Describe how you would prepare a microscope slide of this tissue. *[2]*

iv Explain why the tissue needs to be thin. *[1]*

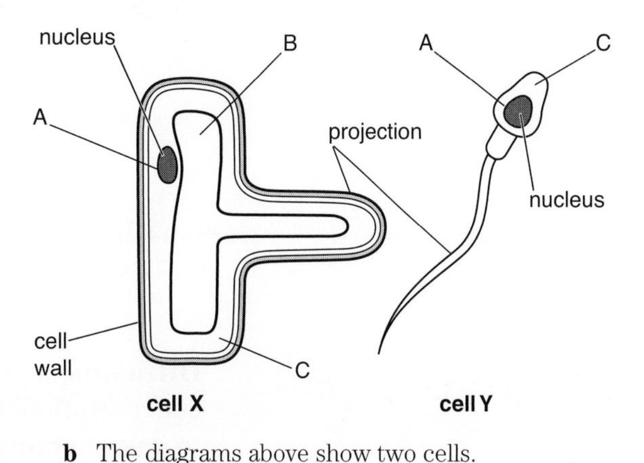
nucleus
B
A
C
A
projection
nucleus
cell wall
C
cell X
cell Y

b The diagrams above show two cells.
Cell **X** is a plant cell and cell **Y** is from an animal.

i Name each cell. *[2]*

ii Name parts A, B and C. *[3]*

iii What is the cell wall made of? *[1]*

The projections in each cell have different functions.

iv Copy and complete the table. *[2]*

Cell	Function of projection	How is it adapted for this function
X	Absorption of water and minerals	
Y		Waves back and forth

Biology Paper 2 Foundation June 2006 (part question)

2 The movement of substances into and out of cells

Diffusion

Diffusion is the movement of substances from high to low concentration. In GCSE questions diffusion is usually linked to **gas exchange** in photosynthesis and/or respiration as shown in Figure 2.1.

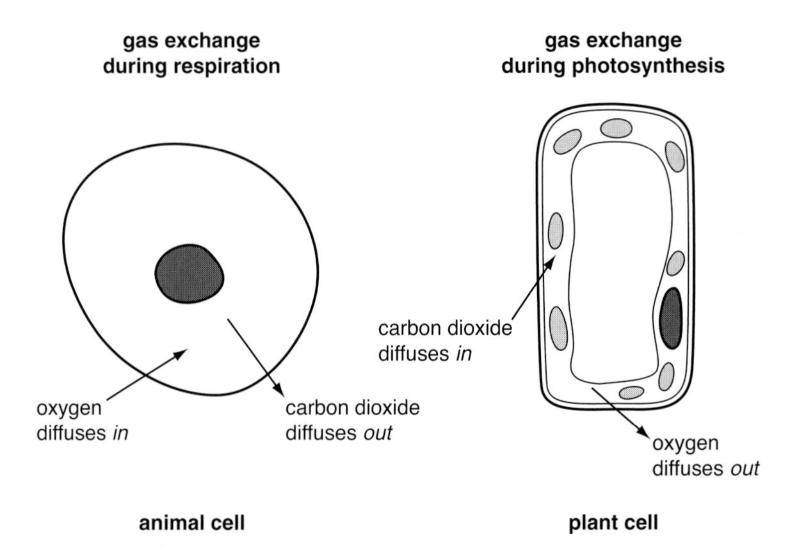

gas exchange during respiration
gas exchange during photosynthesis
oxygen diffuses *in*
carbon dioxide diffuses *out*
carbon dioxide diffuses *in*
oxygen diffuses *out*
animal cell
plant cell

Figure 2.1
Gas exchange and diffusion

Osmosis

Osmosis is a very special case of diffusion that involves the movement of **water**. It is the movement of water from where it is in **high concentration** to where it is in **low concentration** (note: this can be described as moving down the concentration gradient) across a **partially permeable membrane** as shown in Figure 2.2.

Figure 2.2 The process of osmosis

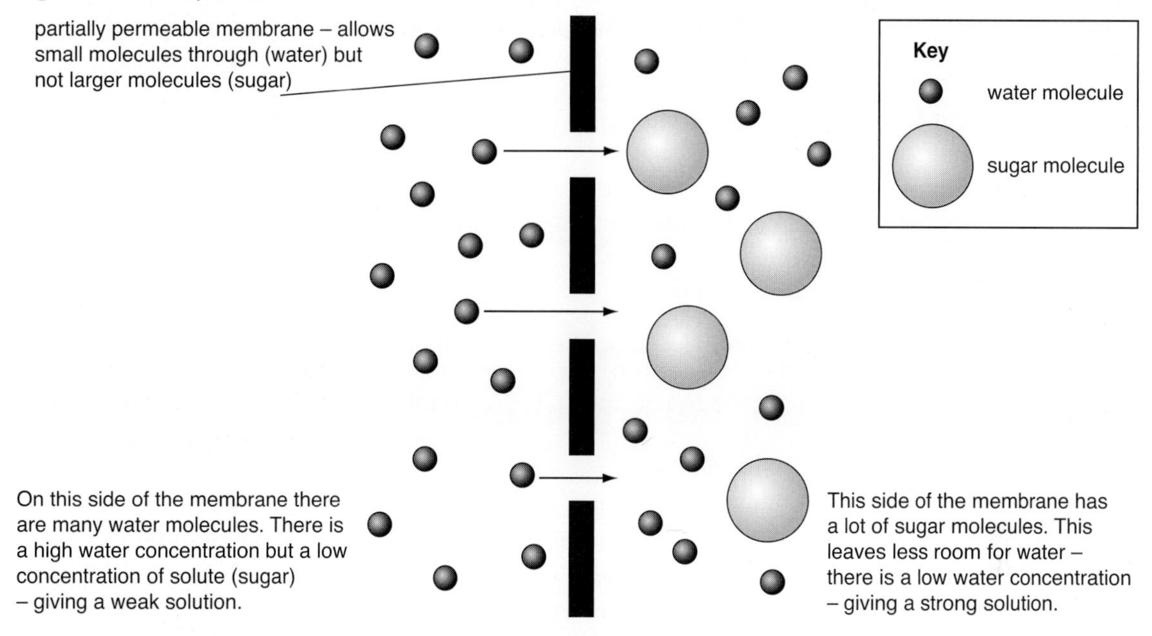
partially permeable membrane – allows small molecules through (water) but not larger molecules (sugar)
Key
water molecule
sugar molecule
On this side of the membrane there are many water molecules. There is a high water concentration but a low concentration of solute (sugar) – giving a weak solution.
This side of the membrane has a lot of sugar molecules. This leaves less room for water – there is a low water concentration – giving a strong solution.

Note: In Figure 2.2 the water moves from left to right by osmosis. Exam questions often give examples of osmosis and ask you to explain what is happening. The following two questions show two ways in which osmosis is examined.

Questions

1 The apparatus shown was set up in a classroom to demonstrate the process of osmosis. Describe and explain what happens after 24 hours. [3]

Visking tubing containing sugar solution

beaker containing water

Typical answer

1 The following three points for 3 marks.

- *There are more water molecules outside than inside the tubing.* [1]
- *Water would move into the tubing and the tubing would expand.* [1]
- *The Visking tubing is partially permeable.* [1]

Note: You had to work out that the sugar solution inside the Visking tubing would contain fewer water molecules than the water outside. Figure 2.2, above, shows why this is so.

You would not get a mark for using the word 'osmosis' in your answer because it was mentioned in the question.

2 Five potato cylinders each measuring 40 mm were placed in concentrated salt solution for 24 hours. When they were re-measured their average length was 37 mm. Explain this result. *[3]*

Typical answer

2 Three of the four following points for 3 marks.

- There was more water in the cells of the potato than in the concentrated salt solution. You could also say that the salt solution is more concentrated than the potatoes. *[3]*
- Water moved from the potato into the concentrated salt solution.
- By osmosis.
- Through a partially permeable membrane.

Note: This time you would get 1 mark for using the word 'osmosis'.

How osmosis affects living organisms

In plants:

- osmosis allows cells to take in enough water to become rigid and provide support – this is called **turgor**
- the **cell wall** is very important because it stops the cell taking in too much water and bursting
- if there is a shortage of water the plant will **wilt** because the cells are not turgid and if the plant loses water (as opposed to not getting enough) the cells may even become **plasmolysed** – the cells lose so much water that the membrane pulls away from the cell wall.

In animals:

- the cells are usually in carefully controlled conditions and they do not take in or lose too much water
- for example a **red blood cell** will shrivel up if it is put in a strong sugar solution and will burst if it is placed in pure water (in the blood it is in a carefully controlled solution and so it normally does not take in or lose too much water).

Active transport

In **active transport**, minerals (or other substances) are moved from where they are **less concentrated** to where they are **more concentrated** – they move **against** the concentration gradient. To do this **respiration** is needed to produce **energy**. **Oxygen** is needed for respiration.

Active transport therefore differs from osmosis in two main ways:

- it moves substances against the concentration gradient
- it requires energy.

Question

1 The diagram shows the concentration of nitrate ions in a root hair cell and in the surrounding soil water.

a Name the process in which nitrate ions are taken into the cell. *[1]*

b Explain why the roots must be well aerated for the process to work effectively. *[2]*

Typical answer

1 a Active transport.

Note: The process must have been active transport as you can see from the diagram that there are more nitrate ions inside the cell than outside it.

b Two of the following three points for 2 marks. *[2]*

- To have access to oxygen.
- For respiration/energy.
- To move the ions against the concentration gradient.

Exam questions

1 The diagram shows a strip of onion tissue placed in a strong sugar solution.

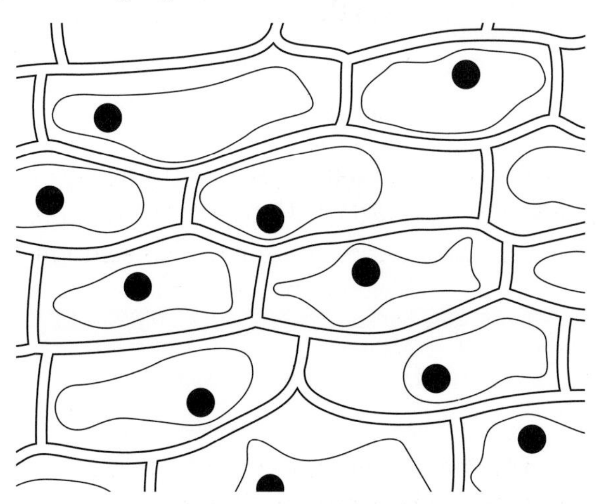

Explain what has happened to cause the changes seen in these onion cells. *[4]*

Biology Paper 2 Foundation June 2006 (amended)

2 Study the bar chart showing the relative amounts of various minerals in pond water and in the cytoplasm of a microscopic green alga (water plant).

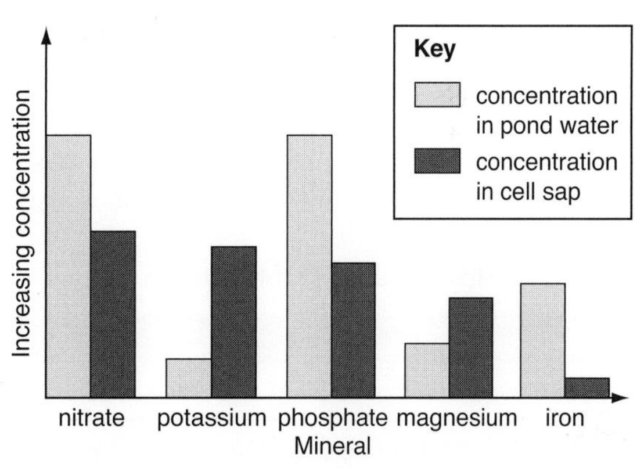
Key
concentration in pond water
concentration in cell sap
Increasing concentration
nitrate
potassium
phosphate
magnesium
iron
Mineral

a Which mineral(s) must have been absorbed by active transport? Explain your answer. *[2]*

b Explain why the rate of active transport increases when the water temperature increases in summer. *[2]*

Double Award (Modular) Module A Higher May 2006

3

Plant nutrition

Plants make food by the process of **photosynthesis**. This process can be summarised by the following equation:

carbon dioxide + water → glucose + oxygen

For this process to happen plants need to trap light energy from the Sun – this is done by the pigment in green leaves called **chlorophyll**.

Photosynthesis experiments

Note: Many photosynthesis questions are based on photosynthesis experiments that you need to know and understand.

Test for starch

One way of showing that photosynthesis is taking place is to show that starch is being produced (usually the glucose that is produced in photosynthesis is converted to starch in the leaf for short-term storage). This is done by carrying out a **starch test** on the leaf. Table 3.1 shows the steps involved in the starch test and the reasons why they are done.

Table 3.1 How to test a leaf for starch

Step		Action
1	Remove a leaf from a plant and place in boiling water.	kills leaf and stops any further reactions
2	Wearing safety goggles boil the leaf in alcohol – this must be done in a water bath with the Bunsen burner turned off because alcohol is flammable.	removes green pigment chlorophyll from leaf (any green colouring masks any colour change with iodine)
3	Dip the leaf in boiling water again.	makes the leaf soft and less brittle
4	Spread the leaf on a white tile and add a few drops of iodine using a drop pipette.	if starch is present iodine turns from yellow/brown to blue/black

Tests to show that light, chlorophyll and carbon dioxide are necessary for photosynthesis

You need to be able to interpret experiments that show that **light**, **chlorophyll** and **carbon dioxide** are necessary for the process of photosynthesis to take place.

It is important to **destarch** the plant – this involves leaving the plant in the dark for at least two days to ensure that all the starch already present in the leaf is used up – before the experiment starts. Figure 3.1 shows the experimental set-up and Table 3.2 gives the results of the experiment.

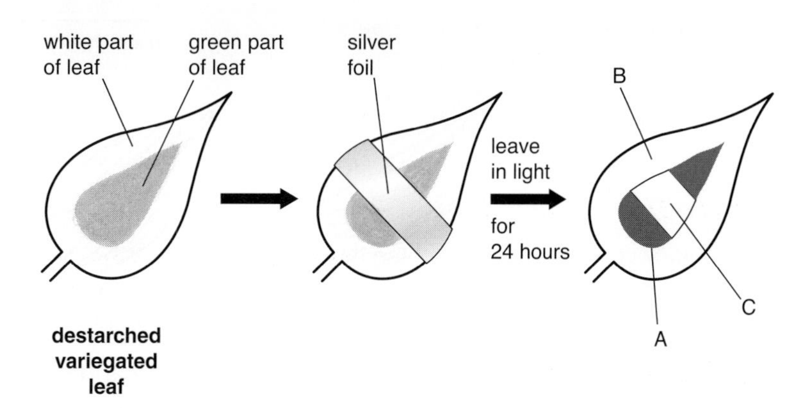
white part of leaf
green part of leaf
silver foil
leave in light
for 24 hours
B
C
A
destarched variegated leaf

Figure 3.1 Showing that chlorophyll and light are necessary for photosynthesis

Table 3.2 Results of the experiment to show that chlorophyll and light are needed for photosynthesis

Leaf section	Result of starch test	Explanation
A	blue/black (starch produced)	this section of the leaf had both chlorophyll (green part of leaf) and light so photosynthesis produced starch
B	yellow/brown (no starch)	no chlorophyll (white part of leaf) – no photosynthesis
C	yellow/brown (no starch)	no light – no photosynthesis

The balance between photosynthesis and respiration

As well as photosynthesising all plants **respire**.

Note: Respiration is covered in more detail in Chapter 5 but for this section it is important that you understand that plants respire *all the time* and that in this process oxygen is required and carbon dioxide is produced as a waste product.

A typical exam question combines the exchange of gases involved in both respiration and photosynthesis as shown on the following page.

Question

1. Describe and explain the changes in carbon dioxide over the 24-hour period shown in the graph. *[4]*

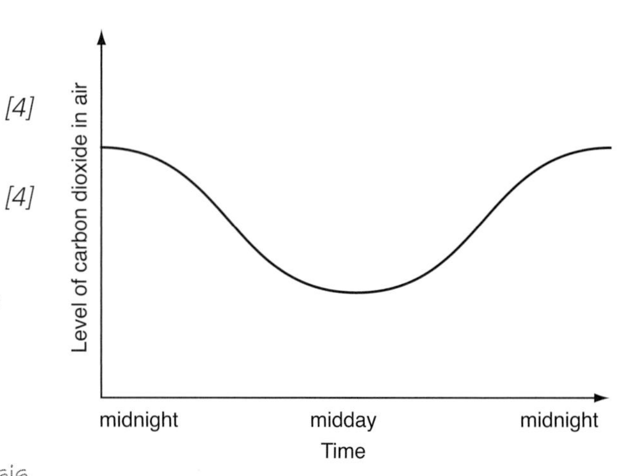
Level of carbon dioxide in air
midnight
midday
midnight
Time

Typical answer

1. Four of the following points for 4 marks. *[4]*
   - Carbon dioxide levels are highest during night/darkness (or converse).
   - During the night/dark only respiration is taking place.
   - This produces carbon dioxide.
   - During the day/light respiration and photosynthesis are taking place.
   - During the day the rate of photosynthesis is greater than the rate of respiration.
   - This causes more carbon dioxide to be used (taken in) by the plant than is produced (given out).

Note: Many candidates will combine these points in one or two sentences in a good answer but in this type of question it is your knowledge *and* understanding of the processes of photosynthesis and respiration that are required to allow you to interpret the graph and gain full marks.

The same knowledge and understanding can be tested in questions involving the colour changes associated with pondweed being placed in **bicarbonate indicator**, as shown in Table 3.3.

Table 3.3 Colour changes of bicarbonate indicator

	Atmospheric carbon dioxide levels	Increased carbon dioxide levels	Decreased carbon dioxide levels
bicarbonate indicator	bright red	yellow	purple

Note: In this type of question involving gas exchange and the balance between photosynthesis and respiration, many candidates make the mistake in answering that respiration in plants only takes place at night!

Factors affecting the rate of photosynthesis

Although you must know that light, chlorophyll and carbon dioxide are necessary for photosynthesis to take place it is important to understand how environmental factors such as light, carbon dioxide and temperature affect the rate of photosynthesis.

The interaction of these factors is summarised by the graph in Figure 3.2.

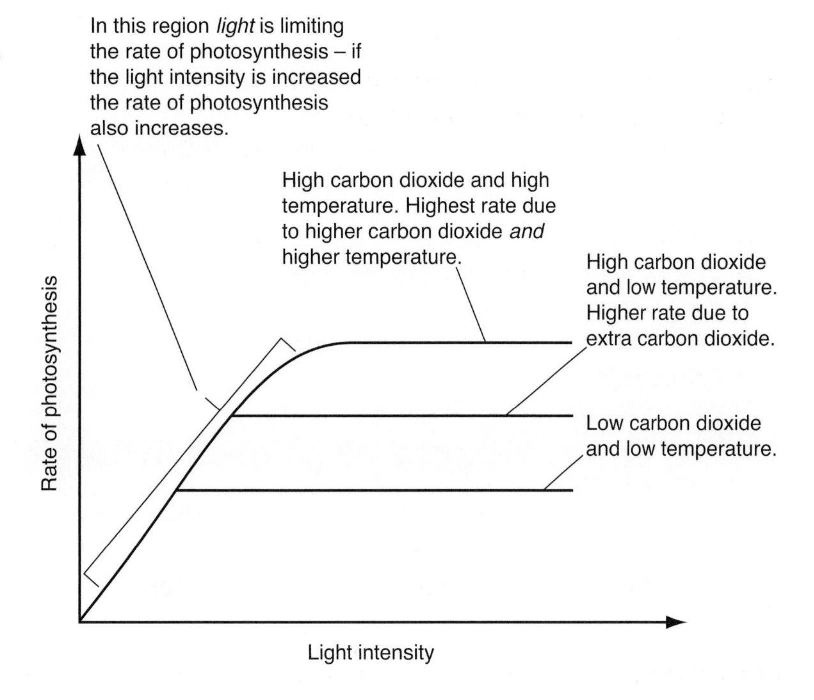
In this region *light* is limiting the rate of photosynthesis – if the light intensity is increased the rate of photosynthesis also increases.
High carbon dioxide and high temperature. Highest rate due to higher carbon dioxide *and* higher temperature.
High carbon dioxide and low temperature. Higher rate due to extra carbon dioxide.
Low carbon dioxide and low temperature.
Rate of photosynthesis
Light intensity

Figure 3.2 Graph to show how environmental factors affect the rate of photosynthesis

Maximising the rate of photosynthesis during crop production

To maximise photosynthesis (and profit) it is important to ensure that plants can obtain all the factors that affect the rate of photosynthesis at their optimum levels, for example light, carbon dioxide and temperature. However it is also important that the plants have sufficient water and nutrients (fertiliser). Important environmental factors can be most easily regulated in an artificial environment such as in a glasshouse shown in Figure 3.3.

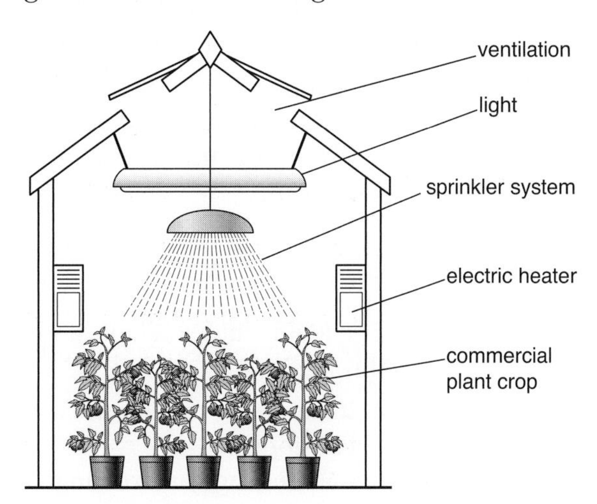
ventilation
light
sprinkler system
electric heater
commercial plant crop

Figure 3.3 Glasshouse

Question

1 a Using Figure 3.3 (on the previous page) explain one way in which the glasshouse is adapted to speed up the growth of the plants. [2]
b What else could be added to further increase the rate of growth? [1]
c What would the owner need to consider to ensure he makes a profit? [1]

Typical answer

1 a Extra light/heat/water; to speed up photosynthesis. [2]
b Fertiliser/carbon dioxide. [1]
c That the higher yield produced compensates for the costs involved in enhancing the environmental factors. [1]

Using the products of photosynthesis

The glucose produced in photosynthesis can be converted to starch for storage but there are many other ways that the glucose can be used and these are shown in Figure 3.4.

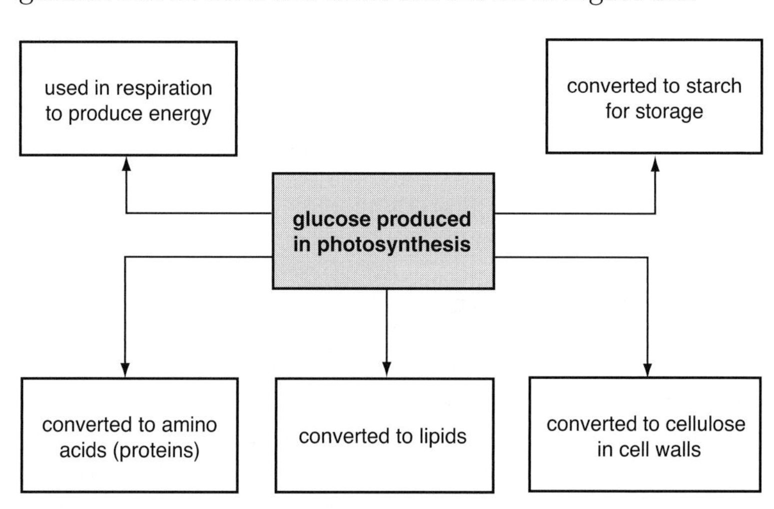
used in respiration to produce energy
converted to starch for storage
glucose produced in photosynthesis
converted to amino acids (proteins)
converted to lipids
converted to cellulose in cell walls

Figure 3.4 Uses of glucose produced by photosynthesis

In addition to photosynthesis plants need to take in the following minerals to maintain healthy growth:

- **calcium** for cell walls
- **magnesium** for chlorophyll formation for photosynthesis
- **nitrogen** (**nitrates**) for amino acids and protein for growth.

The leaf

The leaf is highly adapted for the process of photosynthesis through:

- maximising the quantity of light that can be absorbed by chlorophyll
- maximising gas exchange into and out of the leaf.

The leaf shown in Figure 3.5 highlights some of these adaptations.

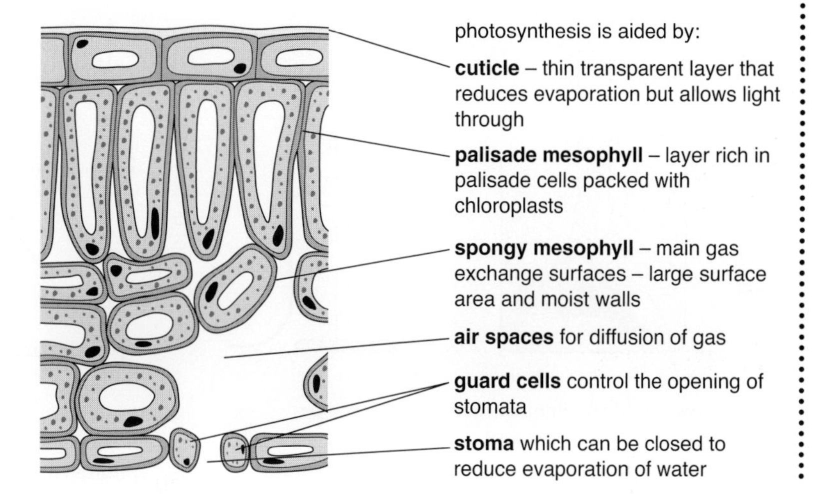
photosynthesis is aided by:
cuticle – thin transparent layer that reduces evaporation but allows light through
palisade mesophyll – layer rich in palisade cells packed with chloroplasts
spongy mesophyll – main gas exchange surfaces – large surface area and moist walls
air spaces for diffusion of gas
guard cells control the opening of stomata
stoma which can be closed to reduce evaporation of water

Figure 3.5 How the structure of a leaf is adapted to aid photosynthesis

The **chloroplast** is a small organelle that is tightly packed with chlorophyll. It is within this structure that light energy is trapped and this provides enough energy to split water. The oxygen produced is released as a waste product and the hydrogen combines with carbon dioxide to form glucose.

Exam questions

Note: In question **1** there are 2 marks awarded for the 'quality of written communication'. In the Biology paper in Double Award Science and in one of the two GCSE Biology papers in your exams you can gain these 2 marks if the quality of your writing is good.

1 The diagram shows apparatus that can be used to investigate the requirements for photosynthesis.

a Describe how a leaf can be tested for starch. *[3]*
Quality of written communication. *[2]*

b Soda lime is used to remove carbon dioxide. Describe and explain the results of a starch test on the leaf shown. *[2]*

c Give **one other** raw material a plant requires for photosynthesis. *[1]*

Biology Paper 1 Foundation June 2006

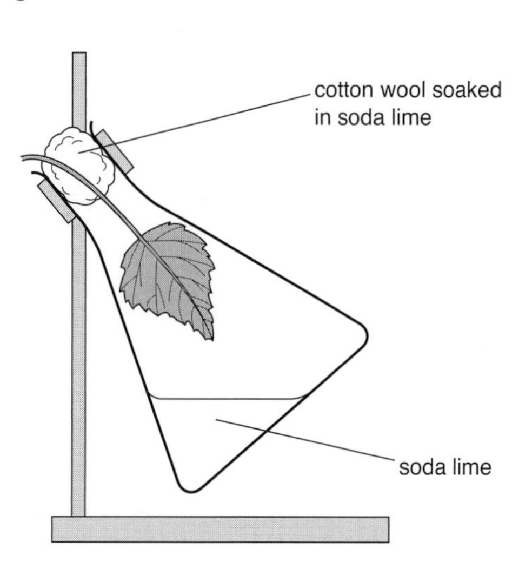
cotton wool soaked in soda lime
soda lime

2 The diagram shows an experiment to investigate the effect of light intensity on the rate of photosynthesis.

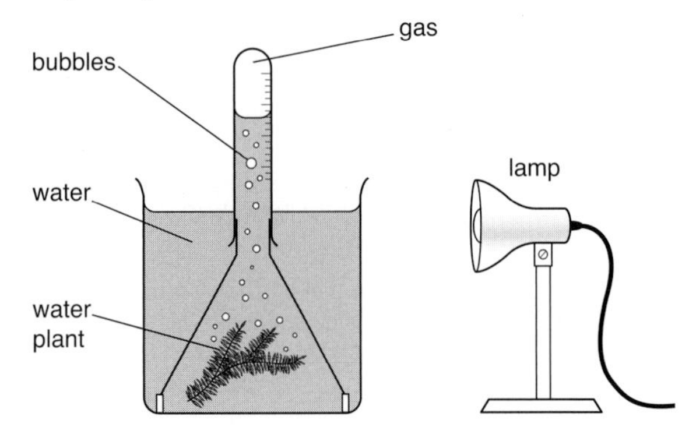
gas
bubbles
water
water plant
lamp

a How could the light intensity be decreased during the experiment? *[1]*

b Name another piece of equipment you would need to measure the **rate** of photosynthesis at a particular light intensity. *[1]*

The experiment was carried out at high and at low carbon dioxide levels. The results are shown in this graph.

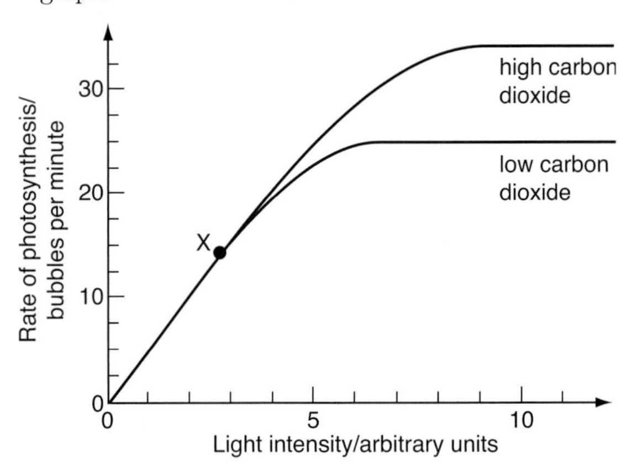
Rate of photosynthesis/ bubbles per minute
0
10
20
30
high carbon dioxide
low carbon dioxide
X
0
5
10
Light intensity/arbitrary units

c Suggest what factor limits the rate of photosynthesis at point X on the graph. *[1]*

d Explain why horticulturalists add carbon dioxide to the air in their greenhouses only when the light intensity exceeds 4 units. *[2]*

Double Award (Modular) Module A Higher November 2003

4

Animal nutrition, enzymes and the digestive system

Why do we need food?

Food is necessary for **energy**, **growth** and **protection**.

A balanced diet

People who have a **balanced diet** are getting all the essential food groups in the correct proportions. The food groups are listed below.

- **Carbohydrates:** these include starch and sugar (glycogen is similar to starch and forms a similar storage role in animals – both are built up from simple sugar molecules). Carbohydrates provide **energy** (sugar is a fast-acting energy source and starch is a slow-release source). Examples of foods rich in sugar are biscuits, cakes, jam and fizzy drinks. Potatoes, rice and bread are all rich in starch.
- **Protein:** protein provides the building blocks for the **growth** and **repair** of cells but can be used for energy when reserves of carbohydrate and fat are low. Protein provides approximately the same amount of energy per gram as carbohydrate. Good examples of protein-rich foods are lean meat and egg white.
- **Fat:** an excellent **energy store**. It provides double the energy per gram compared to carbohydrate and protein. Fat is also important in providing **insulation** and **protects** some organs. Examples of fat-rich foods are streaky bacon, cheese and lard.
- **Water:** is important as a solvent, a transport medium, a component of cytoplasm and body fluids and for its use in chemical reactions.
- **Fibre:** is essential for the efficient working of the digestive system and preventing constipation. It is the cellulose (a complex carbohydrate also built up from simple sugar units) in cell walls that is the main constituent of fibre. Examples of foods rich in fibre are wholemeal bread and green vegetables.

- **Vitamins:**

Table 4.1 Vitamins C and D

Vitamin	Sources	Role in body	Symptoms of deficiency
C	citrus fruit; green vegetables	healthy development of teeth and gums	scurvy
D	fish liver oil; milk, eggs	normal growth – helps in development of bones and teeth	rickets

- **Minerals: calcium** is needed for teeth and bones and **iron** is needed to make haemoglobin which enables red blood cells to transport oxygen around the body.

The elements present in the main food groups are:

- **carbohydrate, fat and fibre:** contain the elements carbon, hydrogen and oxygen
- **protein:** contains elements carbon, hydrogen, oxygen and nitrogen.

Starvation and malnutrition

Starvation is when people do not have enough food to eat and malnutrition is when food may be available but not all the food groups are available (or are not used).

In Britain it is unlikely that people will starve but it is probable that many people are affected by malnutrition.

How much energy do we need?

The amount of the different types of food we require varies during our lifetime. For example we need more protein as a growing child than we need in our old age. Our energy requirement also varies and this depends on our **age**, our **gender** and our level of **activity**.

Obviously there may be an overlap between these, as men are more likely to have physically demanding jobs, so are likely to use more energy than women who may be office based.

Food tests

The tests to identify different food types are shown in Table 4.2.

Table 4.2 The food tests

Food	Name of test	Procedure	Positive result (what happens if the food is present)
starch	iodine	add iodine	iodine turns from yellow/brown to blue/black
sugar	Benedict's	add Benedict's solution; heat carefully in a water bath	solution changes from a blue solution to a brick red colour (a green or orange final colour shows that some sugar is present)
protein	Biuret	add sodium or potassium hydroxide; then add a few drops of copper sulphate; shake	solution turns from a blue colour to a purple/mauve/lilac colour
vitamin C	DCPIP	add drops of the food juice to DCPIP	DCPIP changes from blue to colourless

Enzymes

These are special proteins that help speed up chemical reactions. They are particularly important in the digestive system where they help break down food.

How do enzymes work?

Enzymes are **biological catalysts** that speed up chemical reactions (both breaking down and building up compounds). Figure 4.1 shows how enzymes work.

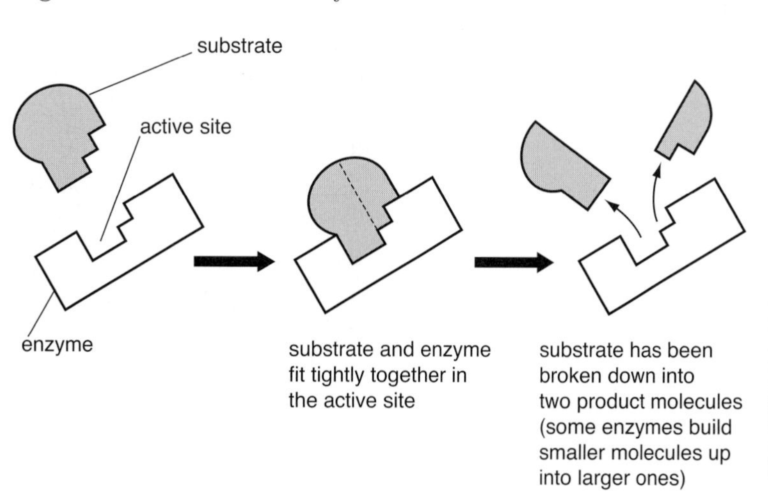
substrate
active site
enzyme
substrate and enzyme fit tightly together in the active site
substrate has been broken down into two product molecules (some enzymes build smaller molecules up into larger ones)

Figure 4.1 How enzymes work

As you can see in Figure 4.1 on the previous page, the active site is complementary in shape to the substrate – they work together like a 'lock and key'. This explains the process of **enzyme specificity**. Each enzyme fits only one substrate (or a very small number) and therefore there is a different enzyme for each reaction.

The effects of temperature and pH on enzyme action

The effects of temperature on enzyme activity are shown in Figure 4.2 and the effects of pH are shown in Figure 4.3.

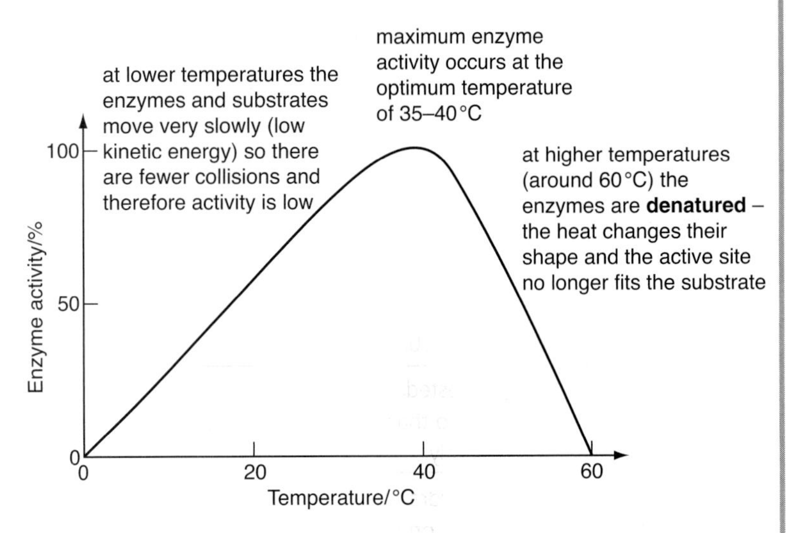
maximum enzyme activity occurs at the optimum temperature of 35–40 °C
at lower temperatures the enzymes and substrates move very slowly (low kinetic energy) so there are fewer collisions and therefore activity is low
at higher temperatures (around 60 °C) the enzymes are **denatured** – the heat changes their shape and the active site no longer fits the substrate
Enzyme activity/%
100
50
0
0
20
40
60
Temperature/°C

Figure 4.2 Effect of temperature on enzyme activity

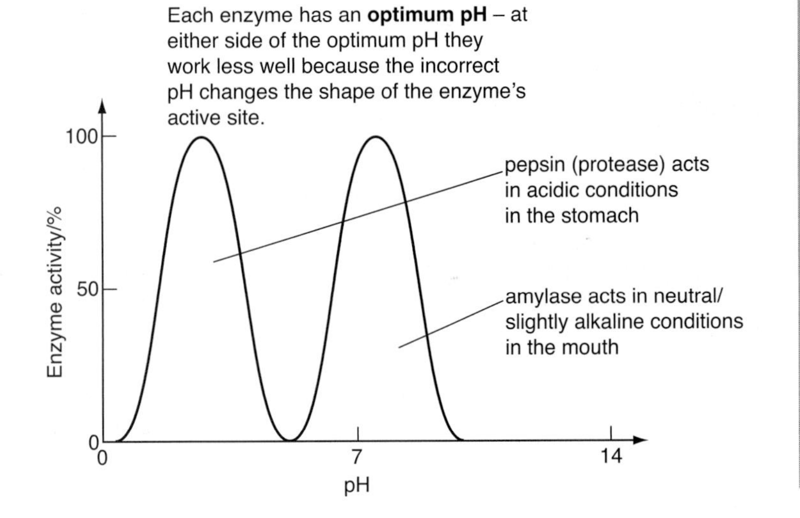
Each enzyme has an **optimum pH** – at either side of the optimum pH they work less well because the incorrect pH changes the shape of the enzyme's active site.
pepsin (protease) acts in acidic conditions in the stomach
amylase acts in neutral/ slightly alkaline conditions in the mouth
Enzyme activity/%
100
50
0
0
7
14
pH

Figure 4.3 Effect of pH on enzyme activity

Enzymes and starch metabolism (an example of enzymes in action)

Starch (which is formed of many joined glucose molecules) is broken down (initially to a double-unit sugar called maltose) and then to glucose itself. These steps are very important in digestion in the body. This reaction is also important in plants in the break down of stored starch for respiration; and plants also carry out the reaction in reverse when they convert glucose to starch for storage.

Digestion and the digestive system

The main processes involved in the digestive system are summarised in Table 4.3.

Table 4.3 The main processes of the digestive system

Process	Function of process	Part of digestive system involved
ingestion	taking food into the body	mouth (buccal cavity)
digestion	breaking down food into small soluble units that can be absorbed into the blood	mouth, stomach, duodenum, small intestine
absorption	absorbing digested food from the gut into the blood system so that it can be distributed around the body	small intestine
assimilation	storing carbohydrate (see the section on insulin on page 64)	liver
egestion	removing undigested food from the body	anus

Looking at digestion in detail

The enzymes involved in digestion and their functions are shown in Table 4.4.

Table 4.4 Summary of enzyme action in digestion

Enzyme	Food digested	Products of digestion	Regions of body	Source of enzyme
amylase	starch	glucose	mouth duodenum/ small intestine	saliva from salivary glands, pancreatic juice (from pancreas) and intestinal juice (from wall of small intestine)
protease	protein	amino acids	stomach duodenum/ small intestine	gastric juice pancreatic juice and intestinal juice
lipase	fat (lipid)	glycerol and fatty acids	duodenum/ small intestine	pancreatic juice and intestinal juice

Although enzymes are very important in digestion, the digestive process is helped by other factors. Three important ones are listed below.

- **Getting the pH right:** an example is the action of protease in the stomach. Acid in the stomach creates an acidic pH essential for stomach protease to work. In addition the food is churned up helping to break it down and helping to mix the enzymes with the protein. (Getting the conditions for enzymes right happens elsewhere in the digestive system – saliva is slightly alkaline which is the pH required for amylase.)
- **The role of bile:** bile is produced in the liver and stored in the gall bladder until it is used. Bile **emulsifies** fat by changing large fat globules into many smaller globules. This increases the overall **surface area** of the fat making it easier for the lipase enzymes to work.
- **Peristalsis:** food is moved along the gut by the action of peristalsis. The muscles immediately behind the food contract and push the food along. This also helps to mix the contents of the gut, making it easier for enzymes and food to make contact.

Absorption

The small intestine is specialised for the process of digestion through being very long which increases the **surface area** in contact with food. The surface area is also increased by the presence of **folds** and by **villi**. Figure 4.4 shows a villus.

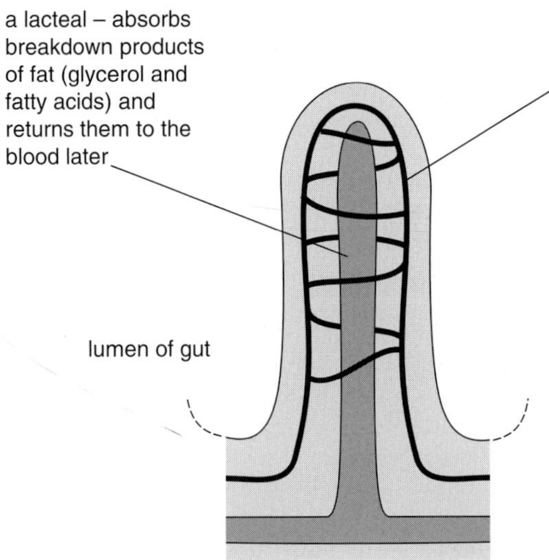
a lacteal – absorbs breakdown products of fat (glycerol and fatty acids) and returns them to the blood later
a capillary network in the villus – absorbs breakdown products of protein (amino acids) and starch (glucose)
lumen of gut
Note:
• how the villus extends into the lumen of the gut which increases the overall surface area in contact with food
• the short distance between the lumen and the capillary and lacteal which speeds up the rate of absorption.

Figure 4.4 Structure and function of a villus

The alimentary canal

The alimentary canal and its functions are shown in Figure 4.5.

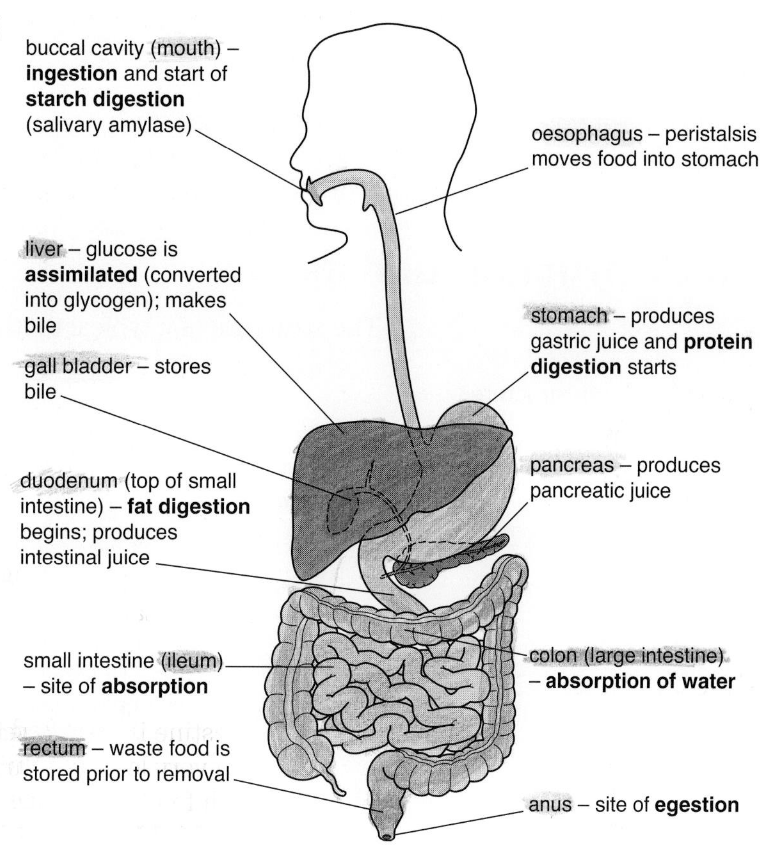
buccal cavity (mouth) – **ingestion** and start of **starch digestion** (salivary amylase)
oesophagus – peristalsis moves food into stomach
liver – glucose is **assimilated** (converted into glycogen); makes bile
stomach – produces gastric juice and **protein digestion** starts
gall bladder – stores bile
pancreas – produces pancreatic juice
duodenum (top of small intestine) – **fat digestion** begins; produces intestinal juice
small intestine (ileum) – site of **absorption**
colon (large intestine) – **absorption of water**
rectum – waste food is stored prior to removal
anus – site of **egestion**

Figure 4.5 The alimentary canal and its functions

Question

1 a Describe and explain how protein is broken down in the stomach. *[3]*
b Describe and explain the role of bile. *[2]*
c Describe and explain one way in which the small intestine is adapted for absorption. *[2]*

Typical answer

1 a Three of the following points for 3 marks. *[3]*
- Broken down by protease/pepsin.
- Into amino acids.
- Stomach acid produces acidic pH for enzyme action.
- Churning action of stomach mixes food and enzymes.

Note: A common mistake is that many candidates answer that the acid breaks down the protein – not true – it creates the right conditions for the enzymes to work in.

b Two of the following points for 2 marks. [2]
- Bile emulsifies fat/breaks fat into small globules.
- To increase surface area.
- For enzyme/lipase action.

Note: Many candidates answer that bile breaks down fat – this is incorrect.

c One point from each of the following for 2 marks. [2]
- Long/folded/many villi.
- For greater surface area for absorption.

Tooth structure and decay

The structure of a typical tooth is shown in Figure 4.6.

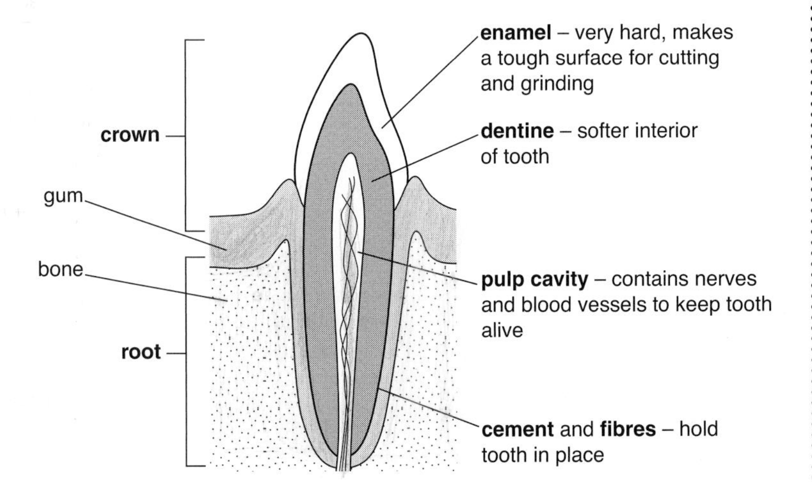
crown
gum
bone
root
enamel – very hard, makes a tough surface for cutting and grinding
dentine – softer interior of tooth
pulp cavity – contains nerves and blood vessels to keep tooth alive
cement and **fibres** – hold tooth in place

Figure 4.6 Tooth structure

Tooth decay is caused by sugar remaining around the teeth providing a food source for bacteria that produce acid. The acid then decays the teeth. Decay can be reduced by cleaning teeth and visiting the dentist regularly, reducing intake of sugary foods (particularly between meals) and using fluoride.

As fluoride can strengthen enamel it is added to many types of toothpaste but is also added to the drinking water in some regions – this has caused considerable debate due to human rights issues.

Exam questions

1 a The table shows some of the nutrients found in baked beans.

Nutrients	Amount per 100 g
protein	4.6
carbohydrate (of which are sugars)	13.1 (5.0)
fat	0.2
fibre	3.6

i Which nutrient is present in the highest amount? *[1]*

ii Give the fibre content per 100 g in g per 100 g. *[1]*

iii Explain why fibre is important in the diet. *[1]*

iv Name **two** other nutrients required for a balanced diet. *[2]*

v Explain why protein is important in a balanced diet. *[1]*

vi Name the **two** substances produced when fats are digested. *[2]*

b Copy and complete the table. *[5]*

		Colour change	
Food nutrient	**Reagent**	**from**	**to**
glucose		blue	
starch			black
protein	Biuret	blue	

Biology Paper 2 Foundation June 2005

2 An experiment was set up to investigate the effect of pH on enzyme activity. The contents of each of the four test tubes used in the investigation are shown in the table. All test tubes were placed in a water bath at 37 °C for 15 minutes.

Contents of the test tube/cm^3				
Solution	**A**	**B**	**C**	**D**
stomach protease	1	1	1	1 (boiled)
protein	2	2	2	2
sodium hydroxide	1	0	0	0
hydrochloric acid	0	1	0	0
water	0	0	1	1

In the test tube where the protein was broken down, the contents of the test tube changed from cloudy to clear.

a Why were the test tubes kept at 37 °C? *[1]*

b In which test tube would you expect the contents to have changed from cloudy to clear in 15 minutes? Explain your answer. *[2]*

c Why would none of the test tubes change from cloudy to clear if amylase was used instead of stomach protease? *[2]*

Double Award (Non-modular) Paper 1 Higher June 2003

5

Respiration

Respiration provides energy. Aerobic respiration can be summarised as:

glucose + oxygen → carbon dioxide + water + energy

The respiratory system

The **respiratory system** provides oxygen (and removes the waste products carbon dioxide and water vapour) in sufficient quantities to enable the body to carry out respiration.

Respiratory surfaces are adapted to aid gas exchange in the following ways.

- The large number of alveoli provides a **large surface area** for gas exchange (as does each alveolus).
- The gas exchange surfaces are **thin** (only two layers of cells separate the air in the alveoli from the blood).
- Through being thin and **moist** the gas exchange surfaces are **permeable**.
- In addition, the process of breathing ensures that the **concentration gradient** of oxygen (and carbon dioxide passing the other way) across the gas exchange surface remains high.

Figure 5.1 The respiratory system

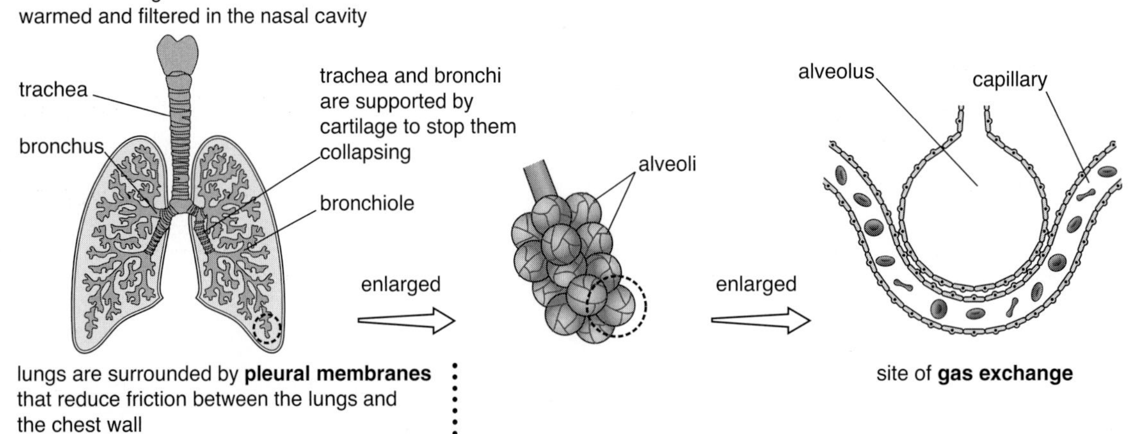
before reaching the trachea the air is warmed and filtered in the nasal cavity
trachea
bronchus
trachea and bronchi are supported by cartilage to stop them collapsing
bronchiole
enlarged
alveoli
enlarged
alveolus
capillary
lungs are surrounded by **pleural membranes** that reduce friction between the lungs and the chest wall
site of **gas exchange**

Note: In general the same adaptations apply to gas exchange surfaces in a plant, for example the spongy mesophyll cells in a leaf are moist and have a large surface area in contact with the air.

The process of breathing

The mechanism of breathing ensures that enough oxygen is provided to the alveoli for gas exchange to take place – the concentration gradient is thus maintained. The processes of breathing in (inhaling or inspiration) and breathing out (exhaling or expiration) are summarised in Figure 5.2.

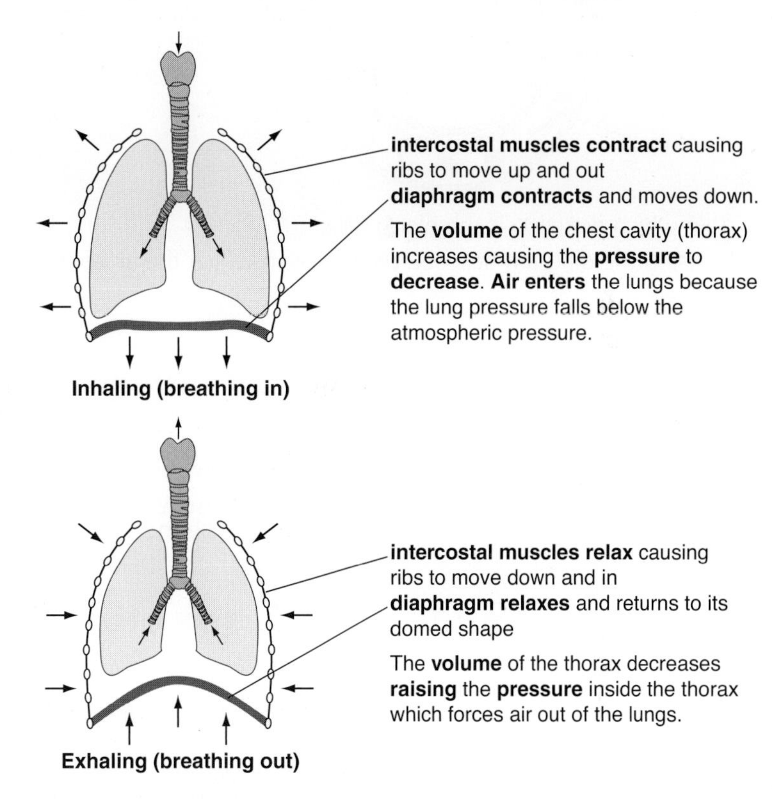
intercostal muscles contract causing ribs to move up and out
diaphragm contracts and moves down.
The volume of the chest cavity (thorax) increases causing the pressure to decrease. Air enters the lungs because the lung pressure falls below the atmospheric pressure.
Inhaling (breathing in)
intercostal muscles relax causing ribs to move down and in
diaphragm relaxes and returns to its domed shape
The volume of the thorax decreases raising the pressure inside the thorax which forces air out of the lungs.
Exhaling (breathing out)

Figure 5.2
Inhaling and exhaling

As a consequence of respiration, inhaled and exhaled air has a different composition of gas as shown in Table 5.1.

Table 5.1 Comparing the composition of inhaled and exhaled air

Gas	Inhaled air/%	Exhaled air/%	Why the change (if any)?
oxygen	21	16	oxygen diffuses from alveoli into blood for respiration
carbon dioxide	0.04	4	carbon dioxide from respiration diffuses from blood into alveoli
nitrogen	78	78	nitrogen is not used in respiration

Question

1 The diagram shows an alveolus and its blood capillary.

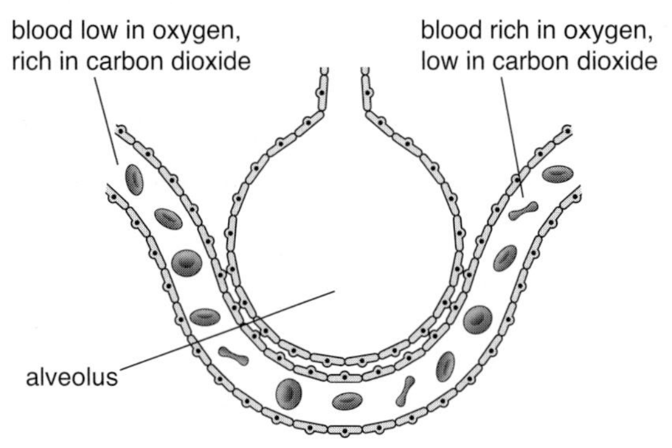
blood low in oxygen, rich in carbon dioxide
blood rich in oxygen, low in carbon dioxide
alveolus

a In which direction is the blood flowing? *[1]*

b Using the diagram describe **two** ways in which the alveolus is adapted for gas exchange. *[2]*

Typical answer

1 a Left to right. *[1]*

b Two from: thin (only two cells between air in alveolus and blood cells)/short distance for gases to diffuse/large surface area. *[2]*

Note: Characteristics of gas exchange surfaces such as permeable/moist/concentration gradient would not count in this question as you cannot identify these features from the diagram. This highlights the importance of reading the question accurately.

Aerobic and anaerobic respiration

Respiration using oxygen is called **aerobic** and respiration without oxygen is called **anaerobic**.

You need to know the process of anaerobic respiration in **yeast** cells (a fungus that is used in baking and brewing). The differences between aerobic respiration and anaerobic respiration in yeast are summarised in Table 5.2.

Table 5.2 Differences between aerobic and anaerobic respiration

Type of respiration	Oxygen used?	Products	Energy produced
aerobic	yes	carbon dioxide; water	large quantity
anaerobic	no	carbon dioxide; alcohol	small quantity

Demonstrating anaerobic respiration

The apparatus in Figure 5.3 can be used to show the products of anaerobic respiration.

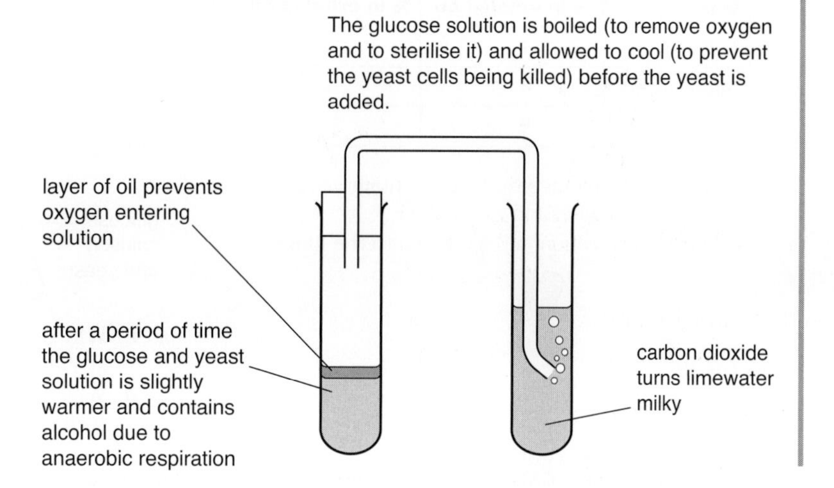
The glucose solution is boiled (to remove oxygen and to sterilise it) and allowed to cool (to prevent the yeast cells being killed) before the yeast is added.
layer of oil prevents oxygen entering solution
after a period of time the glucose and yeast solution is slightly warmer and contains alcohol due to anaerobic respiration
carbon dioxide turns limewater milky

Figure 5.3 Showing the products of anaerobic respiration

Smoking and health

Cigarette smoke produces a number of harmful waste products. The ways in which these can harm the body are shown in Figure 5.4.

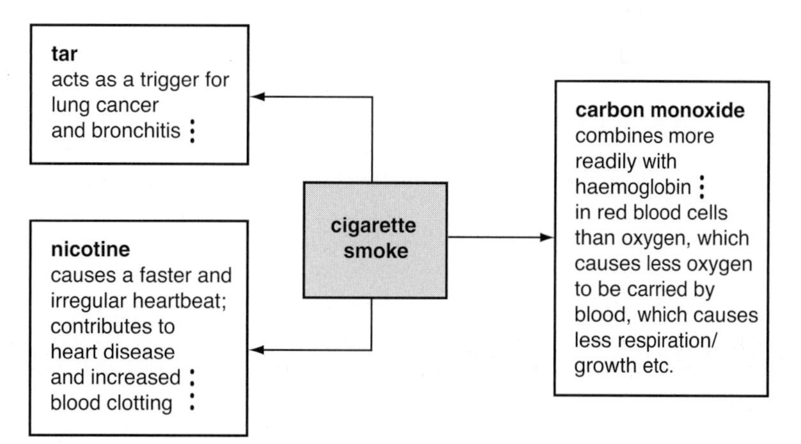
tar
acts as a trigger for lung cancer and bronchitis
nicotine
causes a faster and irregular heartbeat; contributes to heart disease and increased blood clotting
cigarette smoke
carbon monoxide
combines more readily with haemoglobin in red blood cells than oxygen, which causes less oxygen to be carried by blood, which causes less respiration/ growth etc.

Figure 5.4 Cigarette smoke can cause harm

Note: You do not have to be a smoker for cigarette smoke to cause you harm. Breathing in other people's smoke can also cause you harm – this is called passive smoking.

Exam questions

1 The table shows the percentage of gases in inhaled air and in exhaled air.

Gas	% in inhaled air	% in exhaled air
oxygen	21	16
carbon dioxide	0.04	4
nitrogen	79	79

a Explain the change in the percentage oxygen between inhaled and exhaled air. *[1]*

b During inspiration, air is taken into the lungs.

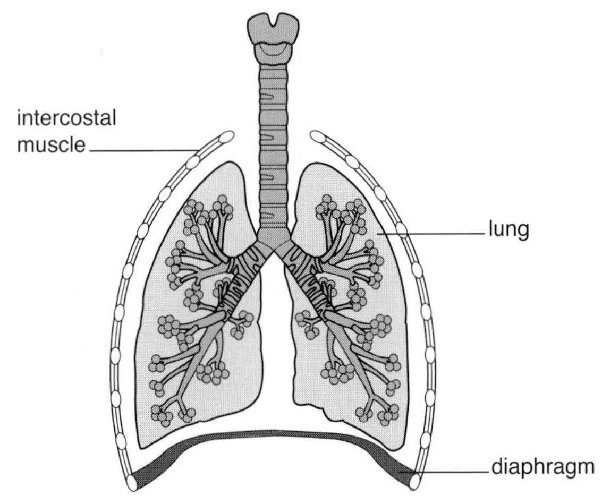
intercostal muscle
lung
diaphragm

Describe and explain the role of the diaphragm in inspiration. *[2]*

c Why does smoking reduce the amount of oxygen carried by the red blood cells? *[1]*

Double Award (Modular) Module A Higher May 2005

2 The apparatus in the diagram was used in an experiment to investigate respiration in yeast cells.

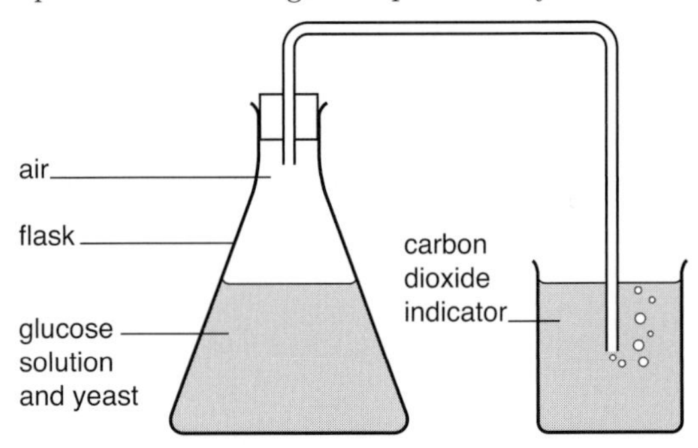
air
flask
glucose solution and yeast
carbon dioxide indicator

a i Why did the yeast cells respire **aerobically** at the start of the experiment? *[1]*

ii What is the advantage, to the yeast, of respiring aerobically rather than anaerobically? *[1]*

b Name a carbon dioxide indicator and describe how it changes colour when carbon dioxide is present. *[2]*

c The experiment was left for 60 hours. Suggest **two** changes that will occur to the contents of the flask during this period. *[2]*

Double Award (Non-modular) Paper 1 Higher June 2006

6 The circulatory system (transport in animals)

The main functions of the circulatory system are:

- **transport**
- **protection**
- maintaining **body temperature**.

The main components of the circulatory system include **blood**, **vessels** (arteries, veins and capillaries) that carry the blood, and the **heart** that pumps the blood.

The blood

Blood is the transport medium of the body. It consists of a liquid called plasma that contains many substances and also some cells shown in Figure 6.1.

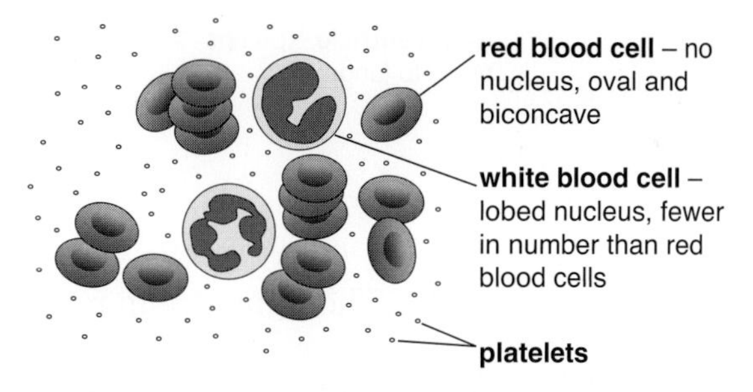
red blood cell – no nucleus, oval and biconcave
white blood cell – lobed nucleus, fewer in number than red blood cells
platelets

Figure 6.1 The main components of blood

The roles of the blood are summarised in Figure 6.2.

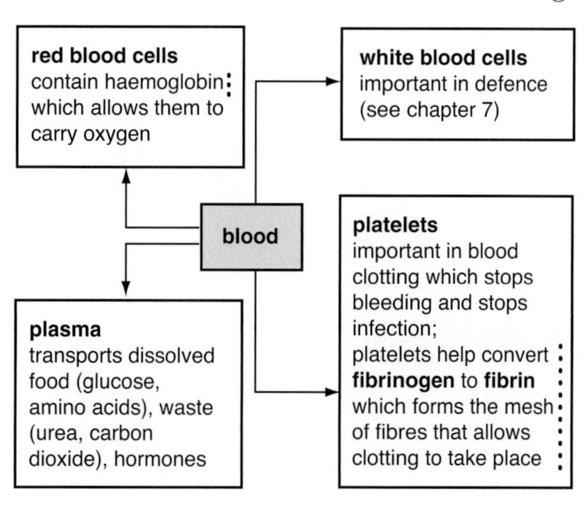
blood
red blood cells
contain haemoglobin which allows them to carry oxygen
white blood cells
important in defence (see chapter 7)
plasma
transports dissolved food (glucose, amino acids), waste (urea, carbon dioxide), hormones
platelets
important in blood clotting which stops bleeding and stops infection;
platelets help convert fibrinogen to fibrin which forms the mesh of fibres that allows clotting to take place

Figure 6.2 What blood does

The heart

The heart is the organ that pumps blood around the body. Figure 6.3 shows that the body has a **double circulation** – the blood passes through the heart twice with each complete circuit of the body.

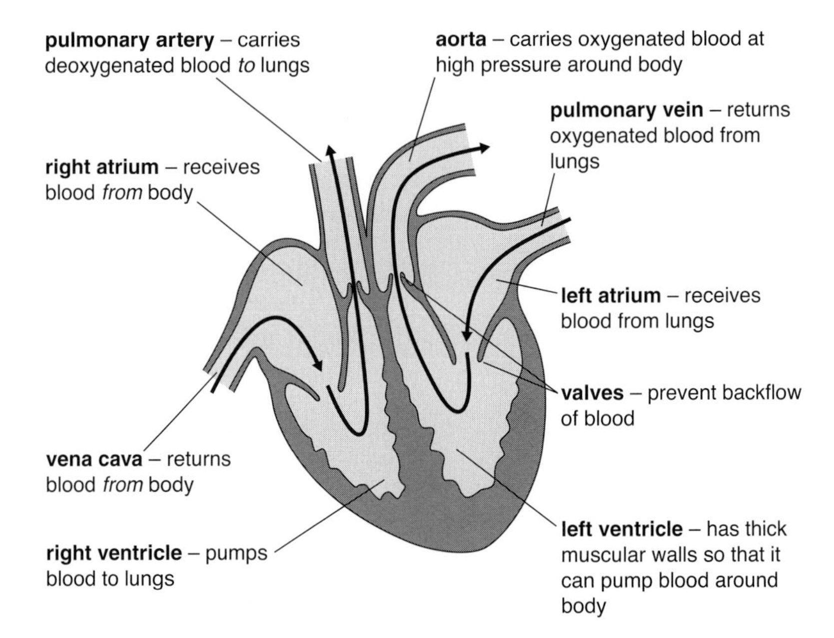
pulmonary artery – carries deoxygenated blood *to* lungs
aorta – carries oxygenated blood at high pressure around body
pulmonary vein – returns oxygenated blood from lungs
right atrium – receives blood *from* body
left atrium – receives blood from lungs
valves – prevent backflow of blood
vena cava – returns blood *from* body
right ventricle – pumps blood to lungs
left ventricle – has thick muscular walls so that it can pump blood around body

Figure 6.3 The double circulation of the heart

Action of the heart

You need to know the sequence of blood passing through the heart. The right atrium receives blood from the body (via the vena cava) and passes the blood into the right ventricle. The right ventricle pumps blood to the lungs through the pulmonary arteries. The pulmonary vein takes the blood back from the lungs and it enters the left atrium. This passes the blood into the left ventricle which then pumps the blood into the aorta and round the body.

The central wall separating the left and right sides of the heart is called the septum. The heart valves listed in Table 6.1 prevent backflow of blood.

Table 6.1 Heart valves and their functions

Valve	Function
tricuspid	prevents backflow of blood from right ventricle into right atrium
bicuspid	prevents backflow of blood from left ventricle into left atrium
semilunar	prevents backflow of blood from arteries into ventricles

The blood vessels

- **Arteries:** these carry blood *away* from the heart. Normally arteries carry oxygenated blood (the pulmonary artery is an exception – study the diagram of the heart to see why).
- **Veins:** these carry blood *back* to the heart. Normally veins carry deoxygenated blood (the pulmonary vein is an exception).
- **Capillaries:** these vessels are very thin – they link arteries and veins together and it is through capillaries that substances are exchanged between the blood and the cells of the body.

All blood vessels contain a single inner layer that is in contact with the blood. This layer is called endothelium (or epithelium) and is specialised in that its cells are very flat and thin making them permeable. The adaptations of the main types of blood vessels are shown in Table 6.2.

Table 6.2 The blood vessels and their adaptations

Blood vessel	Structure	Adaptation
artery	thick walls containing muscular and elastic fibres	thick walls withstand high pressures caused by strength of heartbeat; muscular fibres provide support to withstand pressure; elastic fibres allow arteries to expand as each pulse of blood passes
veins	thin walls; valves	walls are thin as blood pressure in veins is very low (large distance from heart); valves prevent backflow as a result of low pressure; return of blood to heart is helped by gravity (from upper body) and action of muscles pushing on veins
capillaries	walls are one-cell thick	allows diffusion

The main vessels of the circulatory system are shown in Figure 6.4.

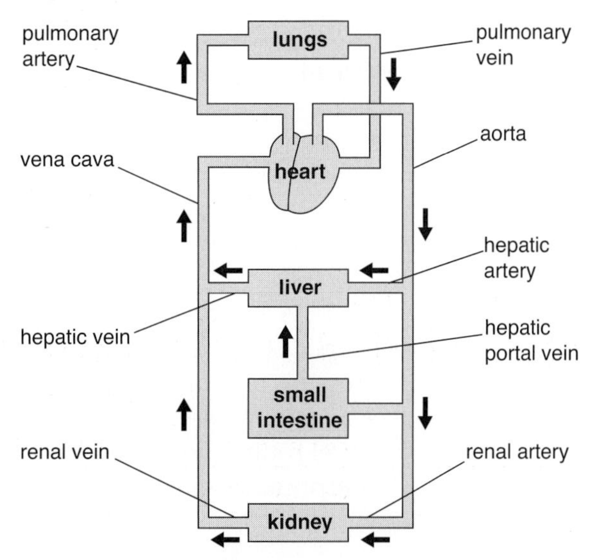
pulmonary artery
lungs
pulmonary vein
aorta
vena cava
heart
hepatic artery
liver
hepatic vein
hepatic portal vein
small intestine
renal vein
renal artery
kidney

Figure 6.4
The circulatory system

The heart and circulatory disease

Heart disease is a very common condition in developed regions such as the British Isles. The blood vessels normally affected are the **coronary arteries** that branch off the aorta and supply blood to the heart muscle. The development of heart disease is shown in Figure 6.5.

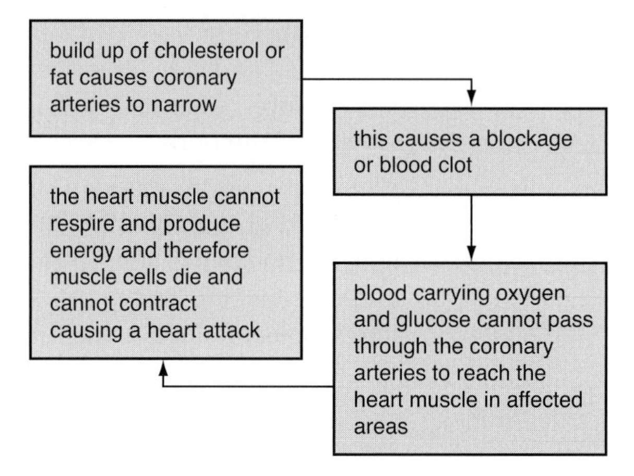
build up of cholesterol or fat causes coronary arteries to narrow
this causes a blockage or blood clot
blood carrying oxygen and glucose cannot pass through the coronary arteries to reach the heart muscle in affected areas
the heart muscle cannot respire and produce energy and therefore muscle cells die and cannot contract causing a heart attack

Figure 6.5 Heart disease

The likelihood of having a heart attack or circulatory disease can be increased by:

- smoking
- eating too many fatty foods
- not taking enough exercise
- genetic factors.

Question

1 Explain how a heart attack occurs. *[3]*

Typical answer

1 Three of the following points for 3 marks: *[3]*

- *coronary arteries*
- *become blocked with cholesterol/fat*
- *this stops glucose/oxygen reaching the heart muscle*
- *no respiration/no energy produced*
- *heart muscle no longer contracts/dies.*

There is a strong positive correlation between obesity and heart disease. People who are obese tend to have high blood pressure and this puts a lot of pressure on the heart as there is a much greater distance over which the blood has to travel round the body. This high blood pressure can be a contributory cause of heart disease.

Exercise can help reduce heart disease as it can help strengthen the heart and allows the heart to pump the blood more effectively. This means that the heart does not have to pump as often in a fit person (of the same size) as someone who is not fit. Thus a good level of fitness helps to reduce the heart rate that reduces the strain the heart is under. Exercise can also help reduce obesity and stress.

The link between plasma, tissue fluid and lymph

Blood pressure forces **plasma** containing glucose, amino acids and other small substances through the capillaries into the tissues. This is necessary as the cells need these substances (and others) to respire and grow; although the larger structures, for example red blood cells, are too large to pass through. The liquid surrounding the cells is called **tissue fluid** and is similar to the plasma in all except position.

Some of the water lost from the capillary passes back into the capillary by osmosis but some is left behind. Excess tissue fluid is drained by the lymphatic system (a system of tubes that links with the circulatory system) and is eventually emptied back into the blood system. When it is in the lymphatic system the liquid is called **lymph**.

Exam questions

1 The diagram shows blood cells viewed at a magnification of 4000 times.

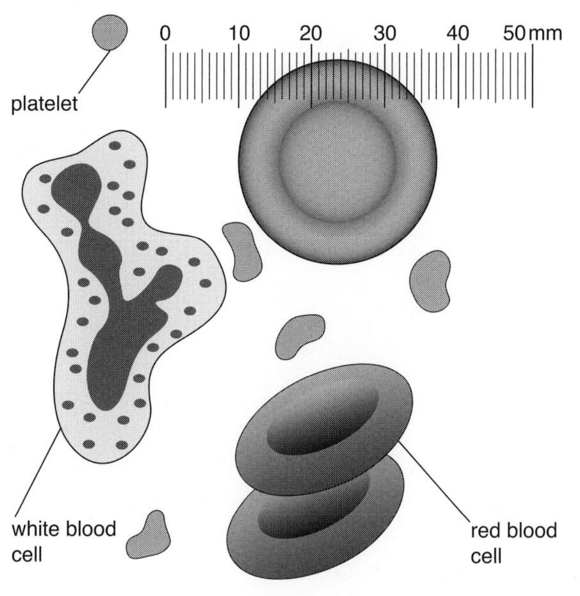
0
10
20
30
40
50 mm
platelet
white blood cell
red blood cell

a Calculate the actual diameter of a red blood cell in mm. *[2]*

b Give **one** function of a white blood cell. *[1]*

c Describe the function of platelets. *[2]*

Biology Paper 1 Foundation June 2004

2 Blood is pumped around the body by the heart.

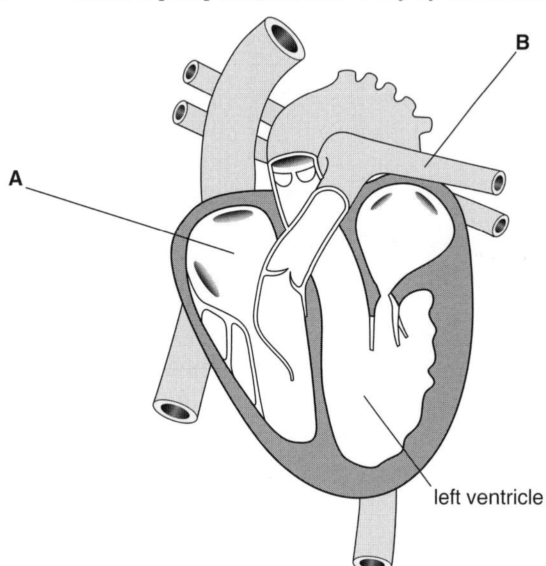
B
A
left ventricle

From the diagram:

i Give the name of chamber **A**. *[1]*

ii Name blood vessel **B**. *[1]*

iii What is the function of blood vessel **B**? *[1]*

iv Name **two** blood vessels, shown in the diagram, which transport oxygenated blood. *[2]*

v Name the liquid part of the blood. *[1]*

Double Award (Modular) Paper 1 Foundation June 2003

3 The graph shows the relationship between blood cholesterol levels and percentage death from coronary heart disease.

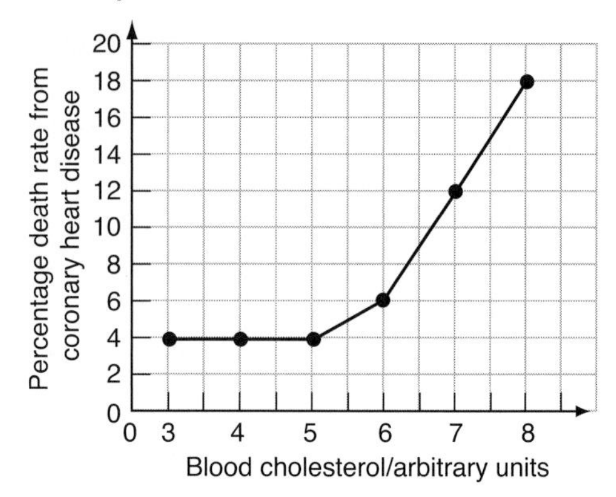
Percentage death rate from coronary heart disease
20
18
16
14
12
10
8
6
4
2
0
0 3 4 5 6 7 8
Blood cholesterol/arbitrary units

a Describe the relationship between blood cholesterol and coronary heart disease. *[1]*

b Which level of cholesterol would reduce the chance of dying from coronary heart disease (in arbitrary units)? *[1]*

c Explain how cholesterol levels can contribute to coronary heart disease. *[2]*

d Give **one** way cholesterol levels can be reduced. *[1]*

Biology Paper 1 Foundation June 2004

7

Disease, immunity and microbes

Defence against disease

The body has a number of defences against harmful **microbes** (**pathogens**). The skin acts as barrier against microbes and the acid in the stomach and mucus and cilia of the respiratory system also restrict their entry. If microbes do enter the body white blood cells can defend in two main ways.

The role of white blood cells

The two types of white blood cell – **lymphocytes** and **phagocytes** – help in combating infection as shown in Figure 7.1.

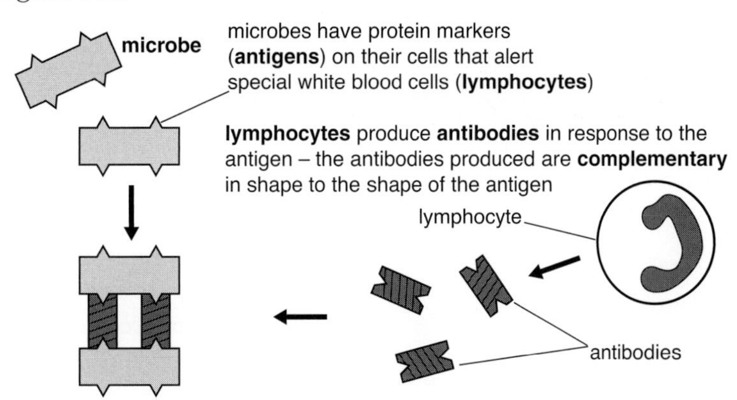
microbe
microbes have protein markers (antigens) on their cells that alert special white blood cells (lymphocytes)
lymphocytes produce antibodies in response to the antigen – the antibodies produced are complementary in shape to the shape of the antigen
lymphocyte
antibodies
The antibodies latch on to the antigens of the microbes causing them to clump together. The immobilised microbes can then be engulfed by other white blood cells called phagocytes. The process of phagocytosis is shown in Figure 7.2.

Figure 7.1 How the two types of white blood cells work to stop infection

Phagocytes can also act by destroying microbes directly (without antibody action) This is called **phagocytosis** and the process is shown in Figure 7.2.

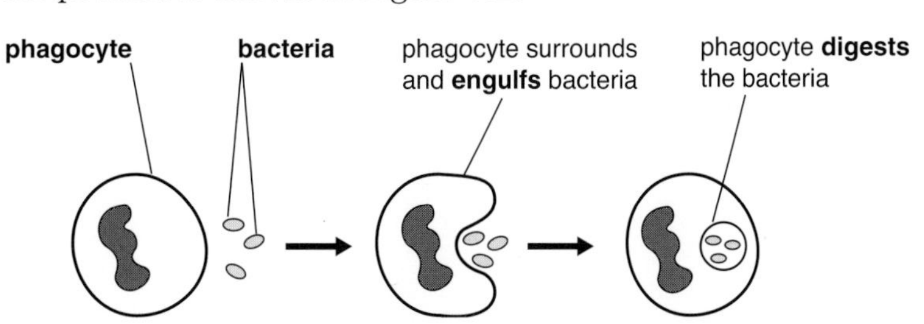
phagocyte
bacteria
phagocyte surrounds and engulfs bacteria
phagocyte digests the bacteria

Figure 7.2 Phagocytosis

Immunity

If a person cannot get a particular disease they are **immune**. Immunity is caused when the body has enough antibodies (or can produce them quickly enough) to combat infection. Figure 7.3 summarises the types of immunity.

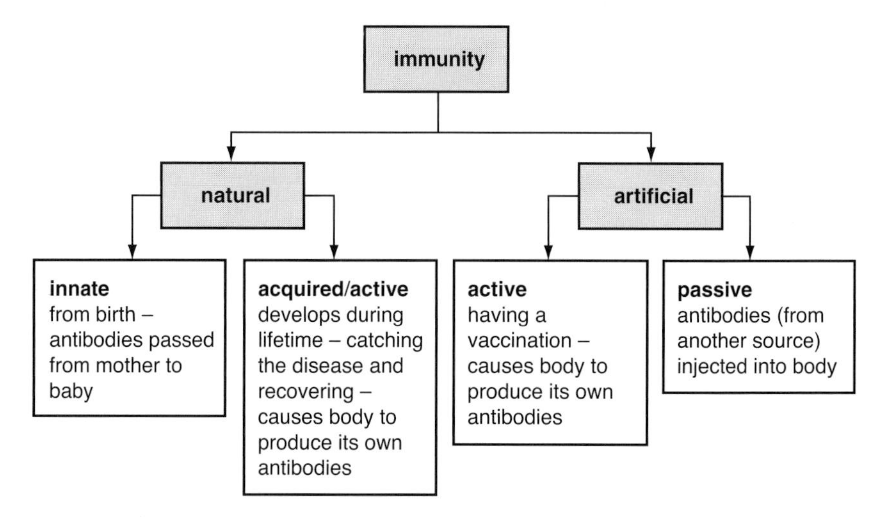
immunity
natural
artificial
innate
from birth – antibodies passed from mother to baby
acquired/active
develops during lifetime – catching the disease and recovering – causes body to produce its own antibodies
active
having a vaccination – causes body to produce its own antibodies
passive
antibodies (from another source) injected into body

Figure 7.3 Immunity

Active and passive immunity

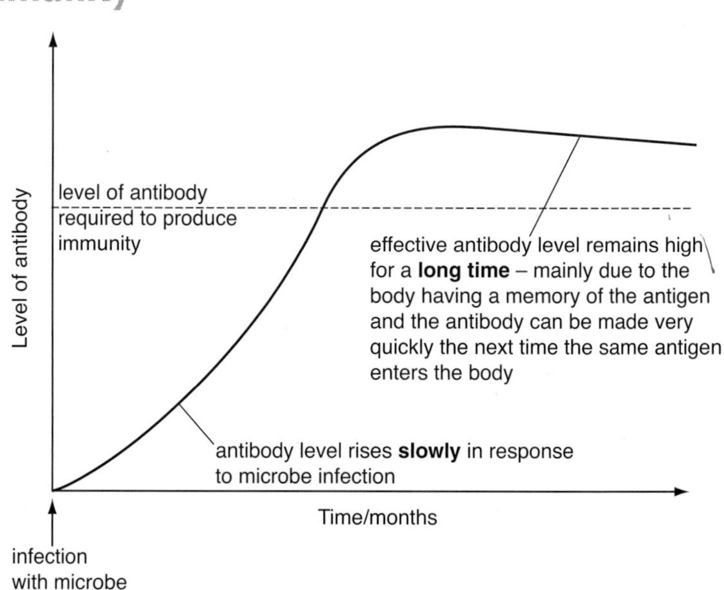
Level of antibody
level of antibody required to produce immunity
effective antibody level remains high for a long time – mainly due to the body having a memory of the antigen and the antibody can be made very quickly the next time the same antigen enters the body
antibody level rises slowly in response to microbe infection
Time/months
infection with microbe

Figure 7.4 Active immunity (acquired by having had the disease)

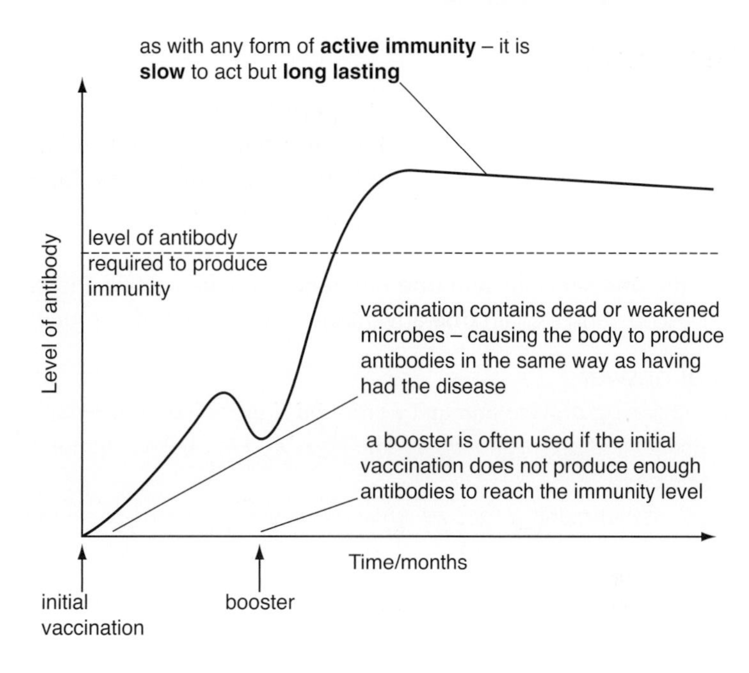
as with any form of active immunity – it is slow to act but long lasting
Level of antibody
level of antibody required to produce immunity
vaccination contains dead or weakened microbes – causing the body to produce antibodies in the same way as having had the disease
a booster is often used if the initial vaccination does not produce enough antibodies to reach the immunity level
Time/months
initial vaccination
booster

Figure 7.5 Active immunity (by vaccination)

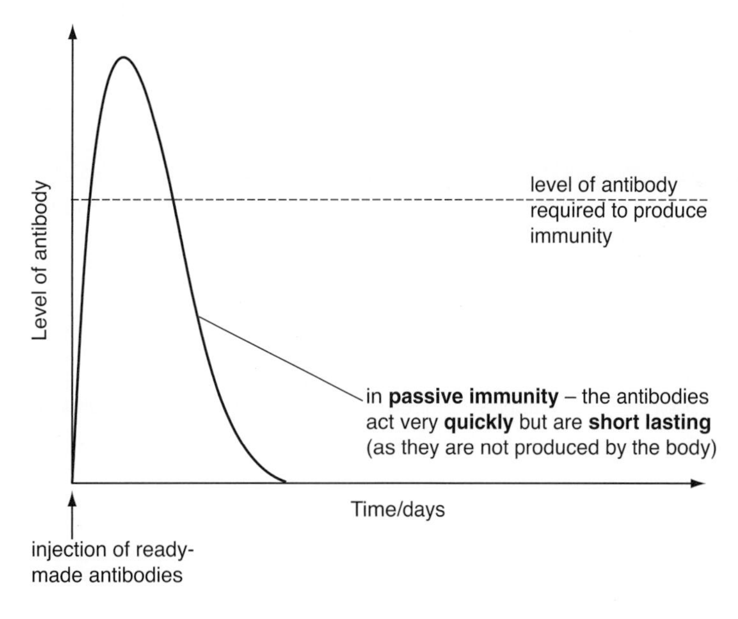
Level of antibody
level of antibody required to produce immunity
in passive immunity – the antibodies act very quickly but are short lasting (as they are not produced by the body)
Time/days
injection of ready-made antibodies

Figure 7.6 Passive immunity (by injection of ready-made antibodies)

Antibiotics

Antibiotics are other chemicals that can be used to treat bacterial infection. They do not work in the same way as antibodies and are usually taken in tablet or liquid form. An example is penicillin.

Antiseptics

Antiseptics are chemicals that can be applied to the skin to kill bacteria. They are used on skin wounds, for example cuts, where the risk of an infection is high. An example is phenol.

Question

1 a State **one** similarity and **one** difference between active and passive immunity. [2]
b Describe and explain **one** advantage of each type of immunity. [4]

Typical answer

1 a Similarity: provide immunity through antibodies; difference: in active immunity antibodies are produced by the body and in passive immunity they are injected into the body. [2]
b Passive immunity: fast as antibodies are ready-made and can act immediately; active immunity: is long lasting as the body has been programmed to make the antibodies and can make them if the same microbes enter the body again. [4]

Disease-causing microbes

Table 7.1 lists some disease-causing microbes.

Table 7.1 Some disease-causing microbes

Microbe	Type	Spread	Control/prevention/treatment
(HIV) AIDS	virus	exchange of body fluids during sex, infected blood	using a condom reduces risk of infection; drug addicts should not share needles; no cure
rubella	virus	airborne (droplet infection)	prevented by vaccination
Salmonella food poisoning	bacteria	from contaminated food	always cook food thoroughly; do not mix cooked and uncooked foods; treatment by antibiotics
gonorrhoea	bacteria	sexual contact	using a condom reduces risk of infection; treatment by antibiotics
athlete's foot	fungi	contact	avoid direct contact in areas where spores are likely to be present, for example wear 'flip-flops' in changing rooms and around swimming pools; treatment by fungicides
tuberculosis	bacteria	airborne (droplet infection)	BCG vaccination; treatment with drugs including antibiotics

Some famous scientific discoveries involving microbes

Jenner and the first vaccination

Jenner noticed that milkmaids who caught the minor illness cowpox did not catch smallpox. He concluded that having had the cowpox gave them protection. To test this he deliberately infected a young boy in 1796 (James Phipps) with cowpox and then deliberately infected him sometime later with smallpox. The boy did not catch smallpox. The cowpox was very similar to smallpox and immunity had built up to both diseases in the boy. This was the first vaccination.

Fleming and the discovery of antibiotics

In 1928 Fleming was growing bacteria in agar plates in a laboratory when he noticed that one of his plates was infected with fungi. He also noticed that around the fungal infection there were no bacteria growing. Fleming concluded that the fungi were producing something that killed bacteria. Fleming was unable to isolate and identify the active agent but later it was isolated and mass produced in1941. This was the first antibiotic and it was named penicillin.

Pasteur and the theory of spontaneous generation

Before Pasteur's famous experiment in 1861 most people assumed that microbes spontaneously appeared from non-living material. Pasteur was able to disprove the theory of **spontaneous generation** by showing that microbes could only contaminate liquids and foods if they were already present or could gain access to the samples. He used specially designed 'swan-neck' flasks in his experiment as shown in Figure 7.7.

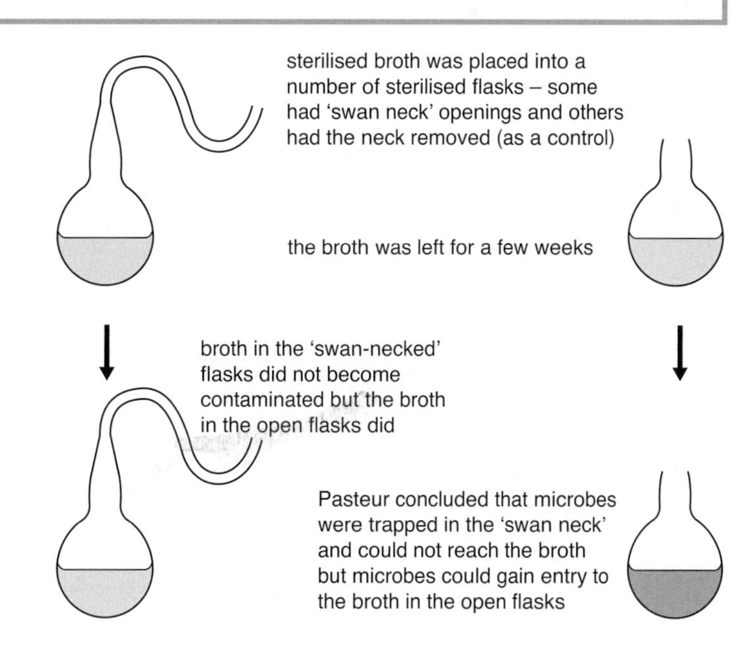
sterilised broth was placed into a number of sterilised flasks – some had 'swan neck' openings and others had the neck removed (as a control)
the broth was left for a few weeks
broth in the 'swan-necked' flasks did not become contaminated but the broth in the open flasks did
Pasteur concluded that microbes were trapped in the 'swan neck' and could not reach the broth but microbes could gain entry to the broth in the open flasks

Figure 7.7 Pasteur's 'swan-neck' flasks experiment

Factors affecting the growth of microbes

Microbes are important in the decay of plant and animal material. They act much more quickly if the following conditions are present:

- many microbes present
- an optimum temperature (usually between 30–40 °C) for the microbe enzymes to act
- the material not being too compacted – if it is compacted it becomes more difficult for oxygen to enter for microbe respiration
- moisture
- suitable (neutral) pH – to provide optimum conditions for microbial action.

Microbes damage food if the food is left in conditions that encourage microbial activity. The principle of **food preservation** is to create conditions that stop or inhibit microbial growth.

Food preservation

Some methods of food preservation are described in Figure 7.8.

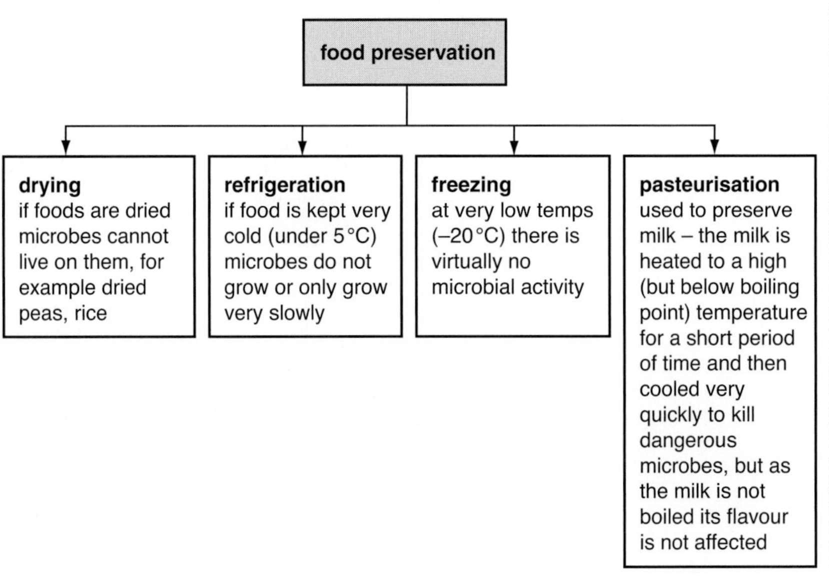
food preservation
drying
if foods are dried microbes cannot live on them, for example dried peas, rice
refrigeration
if food is kept very cold (under 5 °C) microbes do not grow or only grow very slowly
freezing
at very low temps (–20 °C) there is virtually no microbial activity
pasteurisation
used to preserve milk – the milk is heated to a high (but below boiling point) temperature for a short period of time and then cooled very quickly to kill dangerous microbes, but as the milk is not boiled its flavour is not affected

Figure 7.8 Methods of food preservation

Working with microbes in the laboratory – use of aseptic techniques

When working with microbes in a school environment there are important health and safety precautions that need to take place when growing or culturing microbes. These include:

- not eating or drinking in the laboratory
- culturing microbes in sealed containers
- not culturing microbes at body temperature
- using sterile loops for transferring cultures
- flaming the necks of culture bottles to prevent contamination
- sterilising or disposing of all equipment after use
- washing hands thoroughly at the end of the work.

It is very important that the microbes you are working with do not contaminate anything else and the safety measures described above will help prevent this. It is also important that the microbes themselves are not contaminated from other microbes in the air or on surrounding surfaces. The use of **aseptic techniques**, listed above, in the laboratory helps to prevent contamination.

A typical laboratory experiment involves investigating the effect of a range of antibiotics on bacteria as shown in Figure 7.9.

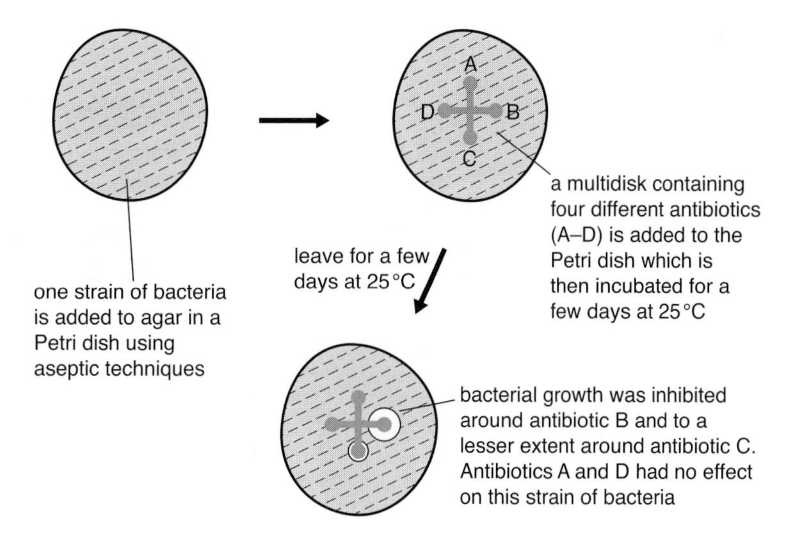
A
B
C
D
one strain of bacteria is added to agar in a Petri dish using aseptic techniques
a multidisk containing four different antibiotics (A–D) is added to the Petri dish which is then incubated for a few days at 25 °C
leave for a few days at 25 °C
bacterial growth was inhibited around antibiotic B and to a lesser extent around antibiotic C. Antibiotics A and D had no effect on this strain of bacteria

Figure 7.9 Investigating the effect of antibiotics on bacteria

Useful microbes

The following list gives examples of when microbes are helpful.

- **Yeast and breadmaking:** yeast respires anaerobically using sugars in flour. The carbon dioxide bubbles are trapped during cooking making the bread rise. Alcohol produced evaporates when heated.
- **Yeast and alcohol:** yeast respires anaerobically using sugars in grapes, barley or hops and produces alcohol and carbon dioxide. It is the carbon dioxide that makes beer or some wines fizzy.
- **Bacteria and yoghurt:** yoghurt is made by bacteria carrying out anaerobic respiration (fermentation) on milk. The bacteria break down lactose in milk to produce lactic acid. The lactic acid makes the milk more solid and gives the yoghurt its characteristic taste.

Useful microbes can be grown in very large numbers using a **biodigester**. Biodigesters can be used to make useful products, for example penicillin, as the microbes can be grown in very carefully controlled conditions. The main features of a biodigester are shown in Figure 7.10.

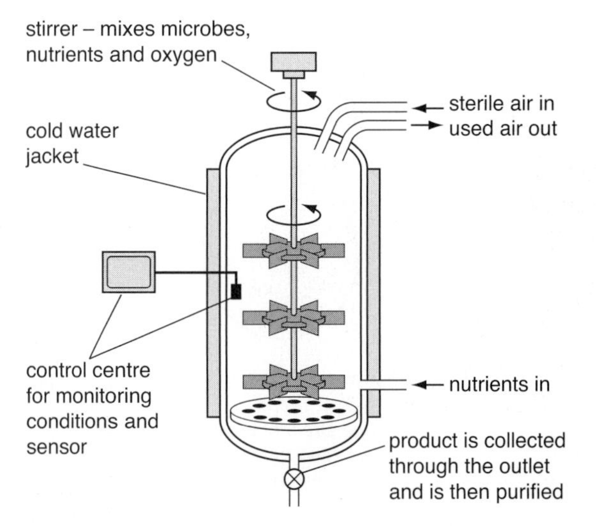
stirrer – mixes microbes, nutrients and oxygen
sterile air in
used air out
cold water jacket
control centre for monitoring conditions and sensor
nutrients in
product is collected through the outlet and is then purified

Figure 7.10 A biodigester

Exam questions

1 The diagram shows the antibody level in the blood of a person who was injected with the micro-organism causing cowpox and later with the micro-organism that causes smallpox.

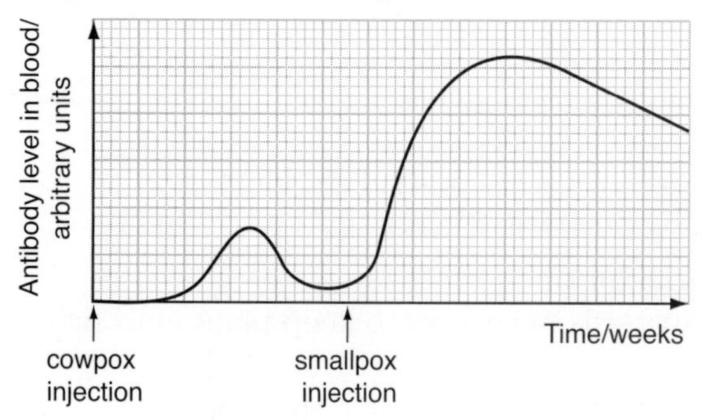
Antibody level in blood/ arbitrary units
Time/weeks
cowpox injection
smallpox injection

a Name the scientist who first carried out such an experiment. *[1]*

b Give **three** differences, shown on the graph, between the antibody levels after the cowpox injection and the smallpox injection. *[3]*

c Explain the response, shown on the graph, to the **smallpox** injection. *[1]*

Double Award (Non-modular) Paper 1 Higher June 2004

2 This mouse is infected with one type of bacterium.

Explain fully how the mouse's immune system combats the bacterial infection. *[4]*

Double Award (Modular) End of Module Test Module A Higher May 2005

3 The diagrams (above, right) show how to sterilise a wire loop used to sample a colony of micro-organisms.

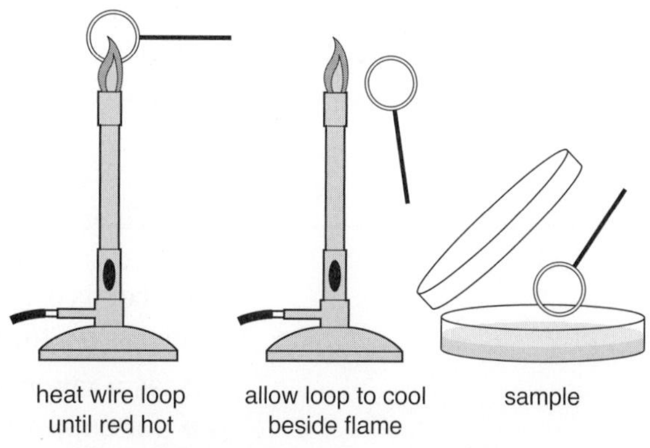
heat wire loop until red hot
allow loop to cool beside flame
sample

a Name **two** types of micro-organism. *[2]*

b Suggest why the loop is:

i allowed to cool before sampling the colony. *[1]*

ii not allowed to touch an unsterilised surface when cooling. *[1]*

c Describe **two** other precautions which should be taken when working with micro-organisms. *[2]*

Biology Paper 1 Foundation June 2006

4 The diagram shows one way of producing yoghurt.

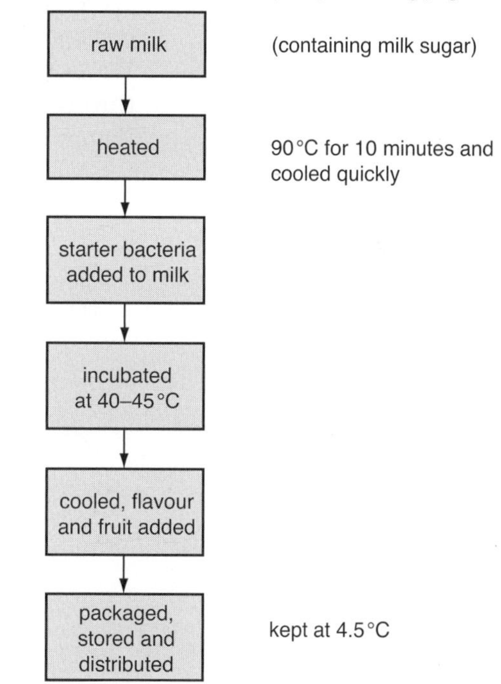
raw milk
(containing milk sugar)
heated
90 °C for 10 minutes and cooled quickly
starter bacteria added to milk
incubated at 40–45 °C
cooled, flavour and fruit added
packaged, stored and distributed
kept at 4.5 °C

a Explain why the raw milk is initially heated to 90 °C for 10 minutes and cooled quickly. *[2]*

b How do the starter bacteria change milk to yoghurt? *[2]*

c Explain why the packaged yoghurt is stored at 4.5 °C. *[1]*

Biology Paper 1 Foundation June 2004

8

Transport in plants

Water is a very important compound in plants. It is necessary for many purposes including:

- as a raw material for photosynthesis
- for support – water is necessary to keep plant cells firm and turgid
- for transport of mineral ions through the plant
- for cooling leaves.

Movement of water through a plant

Water enters the roots by osmosis but needs to be transported throughout the plant to carry out its functions. Water moves from cell to cell by osmosis but is carried through much of the plant by specialised cells called **xylem**. Figure 8.1 shows how water moves through a plant.

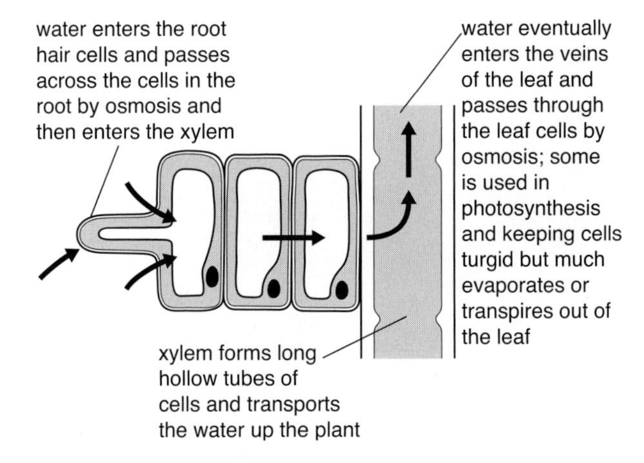
water enters the root hair cells and passes across the cells in the root by osmosis and then enters the xylem
water eventually enters the veins of the leaf and passes through the leaf cells by osmosis; some is used in photosynthesis and keeping cells turgid but much evaporates or transpires out of the leaf
xylem forms long hollow tubes of cells and transports the water up the plant

Figure 8.1 The movement of water through a plant

Transpiration

The loss of water through the leaves of a plant is called **transpiration**. The continuous stream of water into, through, and out of a plant (by evaporation) is called the **transpiration stream**. The water leaves the plant through small pores in the leaves called **stomata** (the stomata are also the route through which gases diffuse into and out of the leaf). This loss of water may seem a waste but it is a necessary process to ensure that the leaves get enough water to carry out its essential functions.

Measuring transpiration

The rate of water loss can be measured or compared in different conditions by a **potometer** as shown in Figure 8.2. This apparatus measures the **water uptake** by a cut shoot. It does not accurately measure the exact amount of transpiration (water loss through the leaves) as some of the water entering the leaves is used and does not evaporate, but it is an excellent method of **comparing** transpiration in different conditions.

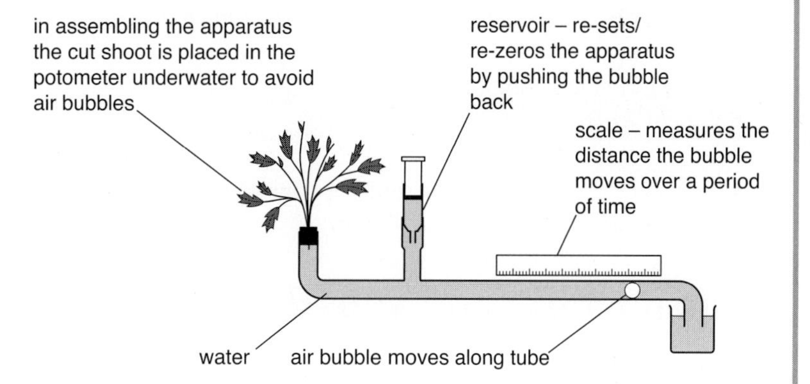
in assembling the apparatus the cut shoot is placed in the potometer underwater to avoid air bubbles
reservoir – re-sets/ re-zeros the apparatus by pushing the bubble back
scale – measures the distance the bubble moves over a period of time
water
air bubble moves along tube

Figure 8.2 The potometer

Factors affecting rate of transpiration

As the following environmental factors all affect the rate of evaporation of water from leaves they also affect the transpiration rate.

- **Temperature:** in warmer conditions water evaporates faster.
- **Wind speed:** evaporation is faster in higher wind speeds as the wind rapidly removes the evaporating water away from the stomata and leaf surface thus maintaining a steep gradient of moisture.
- **Humidity:** humid conditions restrict evaporation as there is a decrease in moisture gradient between the leaf surface and the surrounding air.

The **surface area of leaves** (or number of leaves) affects the rate at which transpiration takes place as the greater the surface area the greater the number of stomata and the faster evaporation takes place.

Note: It is important to know that most stomata are found on the lower surface of leaves as this fact is required in many questions. For example, explaining why water loss is greater from the lower leaf surface.

Question

Note: Typical questions involve interpreting data from potometer experiments or ask you to design an experiment to investigate a factor that affects the rate of transpiration. An example is given below.

1 Describe how you would use a potometer to investigate the effect of wind speed on transpiration rate. *[5]*

Typical answer

1 Five of the following points for 5 marks: *[5]*

- measure distance moved by the bubble
- over specific period of time
- reference to changing wind speed or mechanism of changing wind speed, for example use of fan
- re-set bubble (using reservoir)
- repeat experiment
- compare results
- reference to keeping other factors constant or named example, for example temperature, light levels.

Transport of food substances in the plant

Although sugar made during photosynthesis may be converted to starch for short-term storage it is usually transported to storage organs or growing points through specialised cells called **phloem** by the process of **translocation**.

The arrangement of phloem and xylem in cross-sections of a root and a stem is shown in Figure 8.3.

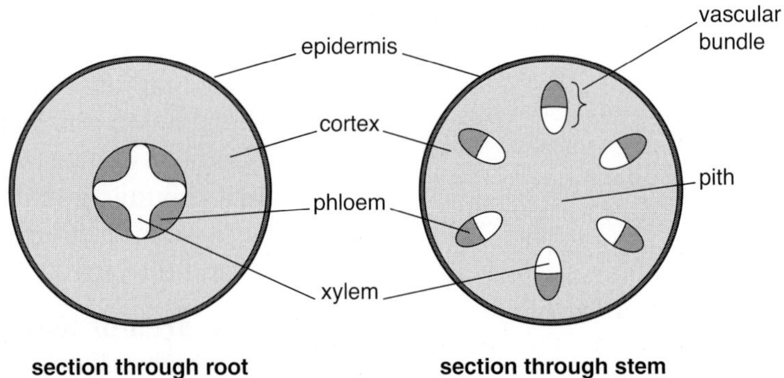
epidermis
cortex
phloem
xylem
vascular bundle
pith
section through root
section through stem

Figure 8.3 Cross-sections through a plant root and stem

The movement of water through and out of a leaf is shown in Figure 8.4.

Figure 8.4 Water movement through and out of a leaf

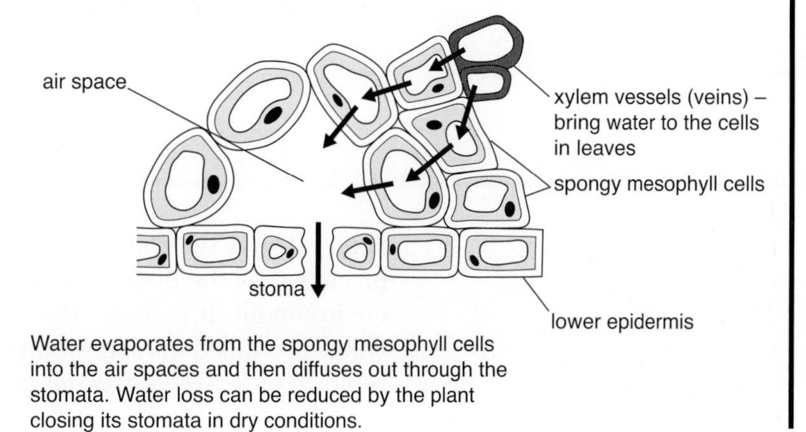
air space
xylem vessels (veins) – bring water to the cells in leaves
spongy mesophyll cells
stoma
lower epidermis
Water evaporates from the spongy mesophyll cells into the air spaces and then diffuses out through the stomata. Water loss can be reduced by the plant closing its stomata in dry conditions.

Exam question

1 a The diagram shows a simple potometer.

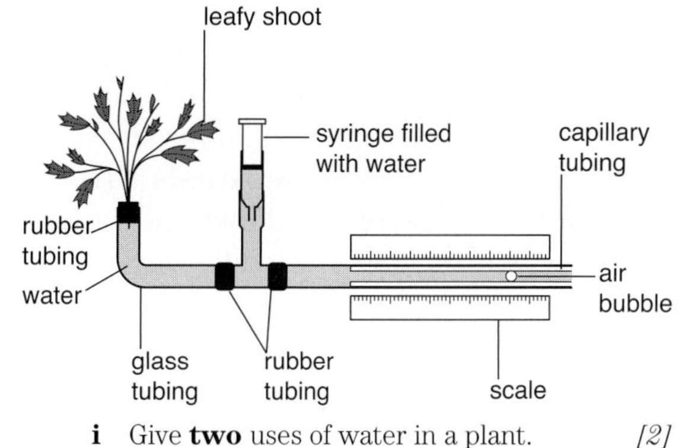
leafy shoot
syringe filled with water
capillary tubing
rubber tubing
water
air bubble
glass tubing
rubber tubing
scale

i Give **two** uses of water in a plant. *[2]*

ii Describe the purpose of the reservoir of water. *[1]*

iii Describe what would happen if the potometer was placed in a warm room for 30 minutes. *[2]*

iv Describe how you would use the potometer to find the effect of wind on the water uptake by the shoot. *[4]*

v Describe a suitable control for this experiment. *[2]*

vi Give **one other** factor which will affect the water uptake. *[1]*

b The table (above, right) shows the average loss in mass of three leaves when hung up to dry, after being treated with Vaseline.

Leaf **A** had the upper surface coated.
Leaf **B** had the lower surface coated.
Leaf **C** had both sides coated.

i Copy and complete the table by calculating the percentage loss for leaves **A** and **B** and adding an appropriate heading. *[3]*

Leaf	Initial mass/g	Mass after 6 hours/g	
A	5	3	
B	5	4.5	
C	6	6	0

ii Which side of the leaf lost most water? *[1]*

iii Explain why the Vaseline reduced the water loss. *[1]*

c Carbon dioxide containing radioactive carbon was given to a plant enclosed in a bell jar. The diagram shows a cross-section of part of the stem.

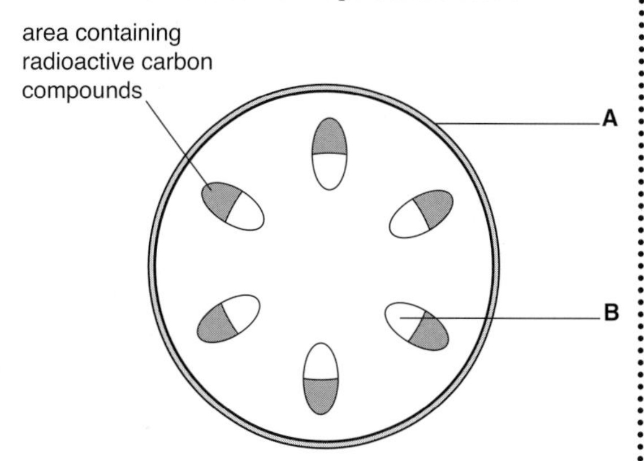
area containing radioactive carbon compounds
A
B

Areas containing radioactive carbon compounds appear dark.

i Name **A** and **B**. *[2]*

ii Describe how radioactive carbon compounds appeared in the shaded areas. *[3]*

Biology Paper 2 Higher June 2003

9

Excretion

Excretion is the removal of waste products that have been produced by the body or toxic materials taken in from the environment. It includes the removal of carbon dioxide and water produced in respiration but does *not* include the removal of food that has not been digested and absorbed.

Note: Do not confuse excretion with egestion.

The main components of the human excretory system and their functions and associated blood vessels are shown in Figure 9.1.

Figure 9.1 The human excretory system

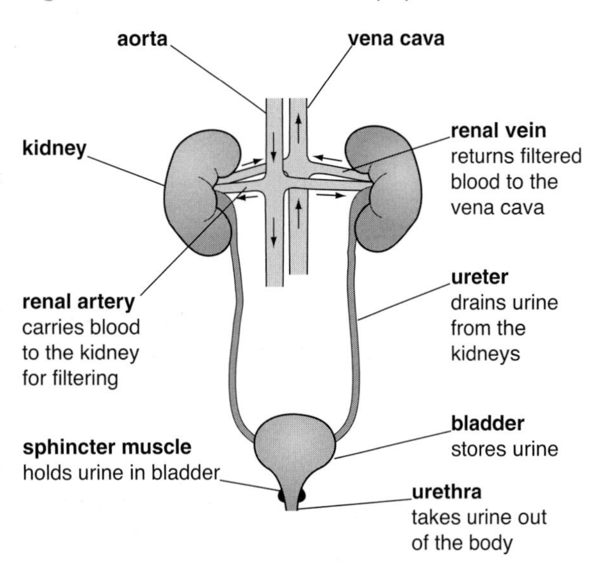

aorta
vena cava
kidney
renal vein
returns filtered blood to the vena cava
renal artery
carries blood to the kidney for filtering
ureter
drains urine from the kidneys
bladder
stores urine
sphincter muscle
holds urine in bladder
urethra
takes urine out of the body

The **kidney** has a very important role in maintaining the internal environment of the body (the maintenance of the internal environment is called **homeostasis**). To summarise the role of the kidney we can look at how it regulates two different substances.

- **Urea:** is formed by **excess amino acids** being broken down by the **liver**. The urea is then transported to the kidney by the blood. When it reaches the kidney a process of **ultrafiltration** occurs. **Urea** (and other waste in the form of salts) is filtered out of the blood by the kidney (the useful materials such as glucose, amino acids and essential salts remain in the blood) and it then passes into a ureter to be excreted.
  The liver also has the important role of the breaking down (or **detoxifying**) alcohol.
- **Water:** is a useful substance and it is important that the kidney controls the amount of water in the body and does not just eliminate it (as it does urea). The kidneys filter out just enough water to keep the blood concentration at the correct level. This process of regulating the level of water in the body is called **osmoregulation**.

Dialysis and transplants

Sometimes the kidneys stop working properly and it is important to undergo **dialysis** or have a **transplant**. In kidney dialysis the work of the kidney is completed by a machine and a transplant involves receiving a proper functioning kidney from a donor.

Each method has advantages and disadvantages. Some of the disadvantages of each are listed in Table 9.1.

Table 9.1 Disadvantages of kidney dialysis and kidney transplant

Type of treatment	Disadvantage of method
dialysis	• requires treatment several times a week and is time consuming – normal life is disrupted • more likely to cause infection • does not work as effectively as a 'real' kidney • important to control the diet, for example a low protein diet helps to prevent the build up of urea • in some areas there is a shortage of dialysis machines • expensive
transplant	• possible that kidney rejection can occur • drugs to suppress rejection need to be taken • involves major operation • shortage of suitable kidneys for transplant

Note: If you are asked a question about the advantages of dialysis these will be the opposite of the disadvantages of a transplant and vice versa.

The mechanism of dialysis

The process of dialysis involves separating the blood from the dialysis fluid using a partially-permeable membrane. Figure 9.2 shows how the process works.

Figure 9.2 Dialysis

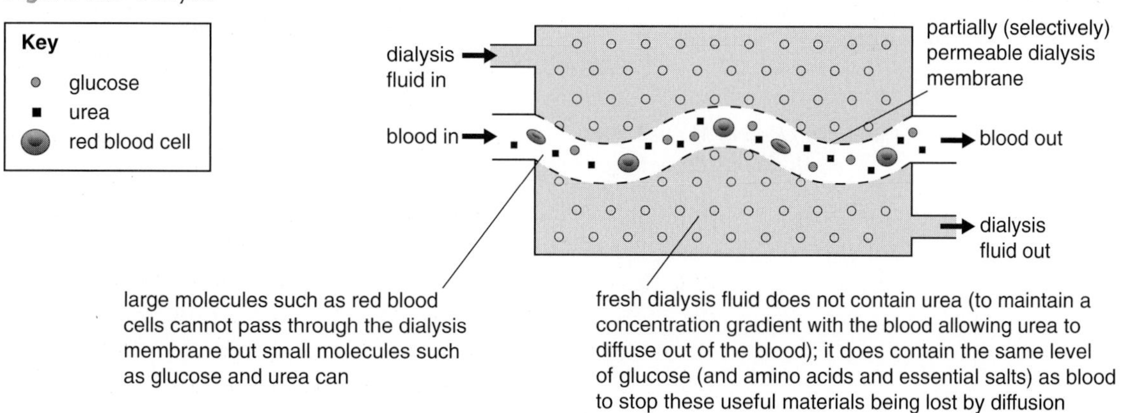
Key
glucose
urea
red blood cell
dialysis fluid in
blood in
partially (selectively) permeable dialysis membrane
blood out
dialysis fluid out
large molecules such as red blood cells cannot pass through the dialysis membrane but small molecules such as glucose and urea can
fresh dialysis fluid does not contain urea (to maintain a concentration gradient with the blood allowing urea to diffuse out of the blood); it does contain the same level of glucose (and amino acids and essential salts) as blood to stop these useful materials being lost by diffusion

Question

1 a Explain why the concentration of glucose in the dialysis fluid is the same as the concentration of glucose in the blood. [2]
b Explain why the dialysis fluid needs to be continually changed. [1]
c Suggest why there are many metres of partially (selectively) permeable membrane separating the blood and the dialysis fluid in a dialysis machine. [1]

Typical answer

1 a To prevent the loss of glucose from the blood [1]; by diffusion [1].
b To maintain the high concentration gradient of urea (between the blood and dialysis fluid) or to prevent a build up of urea in the dialysis fluid. [1]
c To increase the surface area across which diffusion can occur. [1]

Exam questions

1 A diagram of the excretory system is shown below.

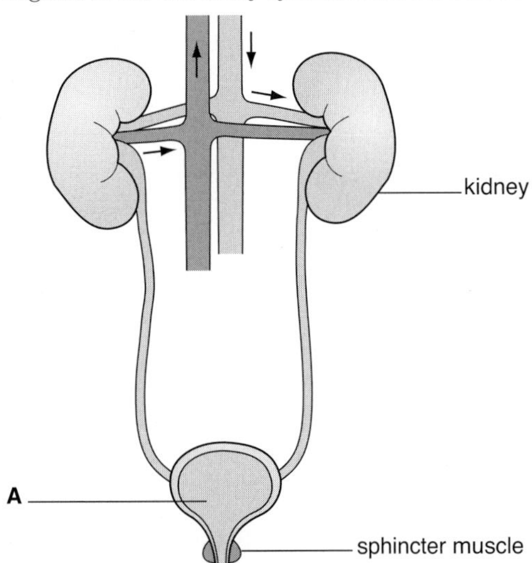
kidney
A
sphincter muscle

a Name part **A**. [1]
b What is the function of the sphincter muscle? [1]
c Copy the diagram and show with the letter 'R' on the diagram the position of the renal artery. [1]
d Define excretion. [1]

Double Award (Modular) End of Module Test Module A Foundation May 2004

2 The diagram shows a kidney machine.

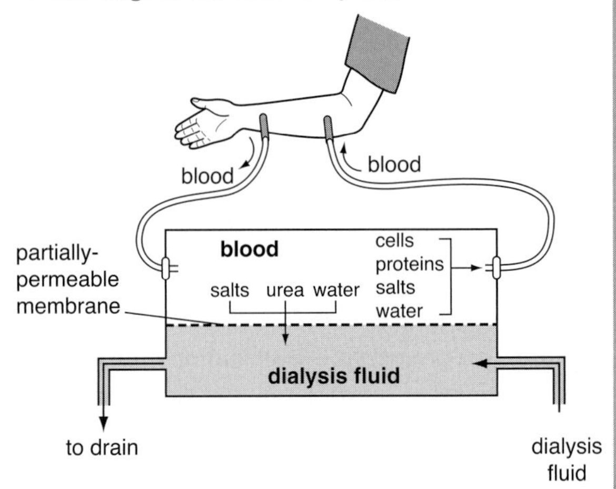
blood
blood
partially-permeable membrane
blood
cells
proteins
salts urea water
salts
water
dialysis fluid
to drain
dialysis fluid

a Name the process involved in the removal of wastes, such as urea, by the kidney machine. [1]
b Why do proteins not pass into the dialysis fluid? [1]
c Explain why the dialysis fluid entering the kidney machine contains **some** salts. [1]
d Explain why there needs to be a continuous flow of dialysis fluid through the kidney machine. [1]
e **i** Where in the body is urea produced? [1]
ii What substance is broken down to produce urea? [1]

Double Award (Non-modular) Paper 1 Higher June 2006

10 Sensitivity and response in plants and animals

Plants

Plants, like animals, respond to changes in the environment that affect them. Plants are particularly sensitive to light and their response to light is called **phototropism**.

Figure 10.1 shows the process of phototropism.

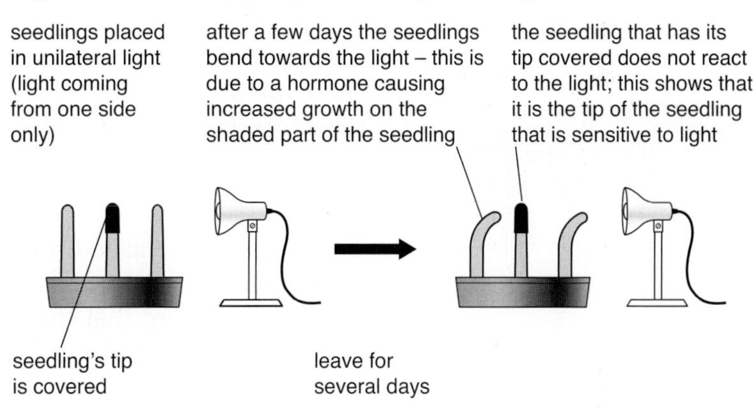
seedlings placed in unilateral light (light coming from one side only)
after a few days the seedlings bend towards the light – this is due to a hormone causing increased growth on the shaded part of the seedling
the seedling that has its tip covered does not react to the light; this shows that it is the tip of the seedling that is sensitive to light
seedling's tip is covered
leave for several days

Figure 10.1 Phototropism

The hormone that produces bending in the direction of light is called auxin and the response has the following benefits to the plant:

more light available → more photosynthesis → more growth

The commercial use of plant hormones

Plant hormones (including auxins) can be synthetically produced and used in the applications shown in Table 10.1.

Table 10.1 Uses of synthetic plant hormones

Application	Method of action of synthetic plant hormone	Advantage
weedkillers	causes plants to grow in such a rapid and uncontrolled way that they disintegrate	most weedkillers are selective – they act on broadleaved plants (weeds) but not on narrow-leaved grasses and cereals
promoting flowering and fruit formation	stimulates flowering; also promotes seed and fruit production	large quantities of fruit produced even when natural pollinators are low in number or the weather is poor; also important in the production of seedless grapes

Animals

A typical sequence of events in the human nervous system is shown in Figure 10.2.

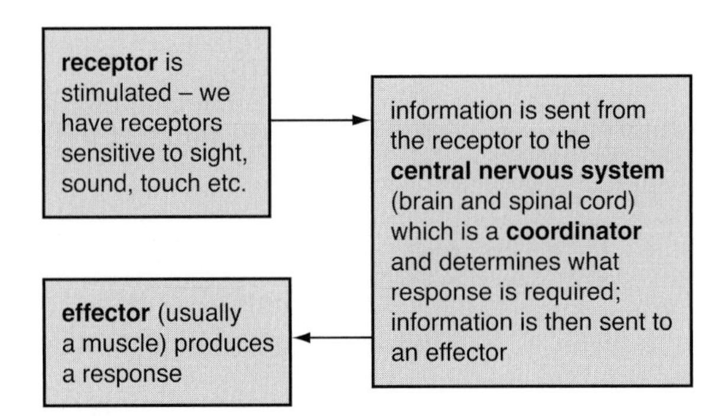
receptor is stimulated – we have receptors sensitive to sight, sound, touch etc.
information is sent from the receptor to the **central nervous system** (brain and spinal cord) which is a **coordinator** and determines what response is required; information is then sent to an effector
effector (usually a muscle) produces a response

Figure 10.2 The human nervous system

The arrows in Figure 10.2 represent the nerve cells (**neurones**) that carry the information between the receptors, coordinator and effectors.

The eye

The eye is a specialised sense organ that contains **receptors** that are sensitive to light. The eye is primarily adapted to ensure that the optimum intensity of light is focused on the **retina** (where the light-sensitive cells are located). Figure 10.3 summarises the structure and function of the eye.

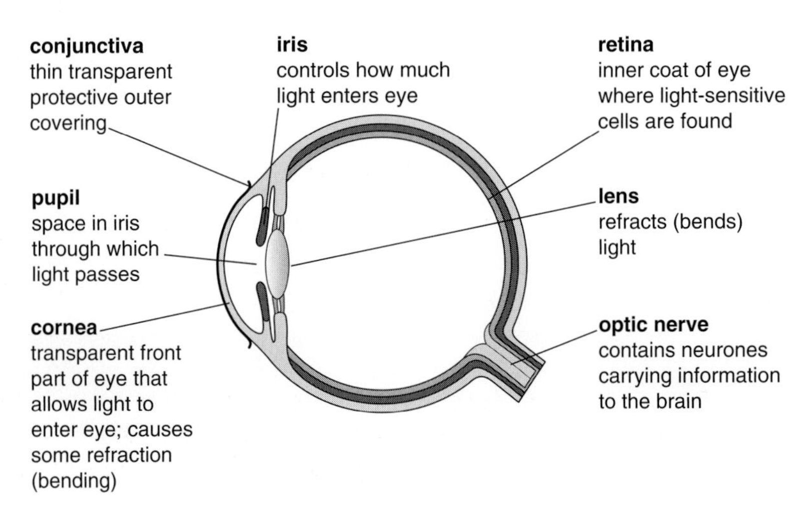
conjunctiva thin transparent protective outer covering
iris controls how much light enters eye
retina inner coat of eye where light-sensitive cells are found
pupil space in iris through which light passes
lens refracts (bends) light
cornea transparent front part of eye that allows light to enter eye; causes some refraction (bending)
optic nerve contains neurones carrying information to the brain

Figure 10.3 Structure and function of the eye

The watery fluid (aqueous humour) between the cornea and the lens and between the lens and the retina (vitreous humour) keeps the lens in shape and allows light through.

The iris muscles contract or relax to control the diameter of the pupil. This in turn controls the amount of light entering the eye.

- In bright light the pupil is narrowed to prevent too much light entering the eye and damaging the retina.
- In poor light the pupil is made larger to allow enough light to enter the eye in order that the object can be clearly seen.

The iris consists of two types of muscle – radial and circular (radial muscles are like the spokes of a wheel moving out from the edge of the pupil and circular muscles form rings around the pupil).

- In dim light the radial muscles contract (and the circular muscles relax) – this makes the pupil larger.
- In bright light the radial muscles relax (and the circular muscles contract) – this makes the pupil smaller.

The eye focuses light by changing the shape of the lens as shown in Figure 10.4.

Figure 10.4
The eye and focusing

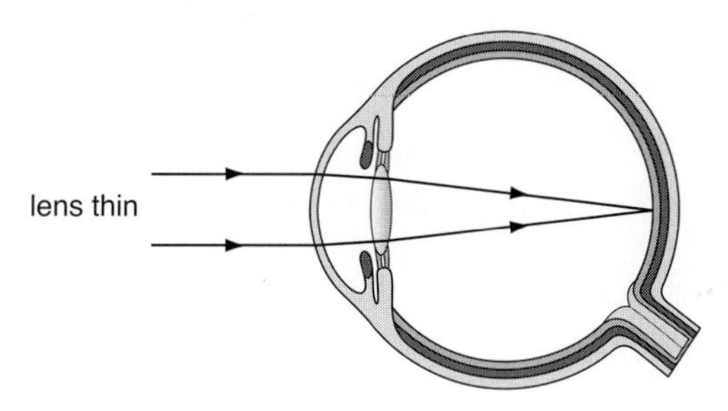
lens thin
light rays arrive parallel; cornea refracts rays; lens is thin as little additional refracting is necessary to focus light on the retina
eye focused on distant object

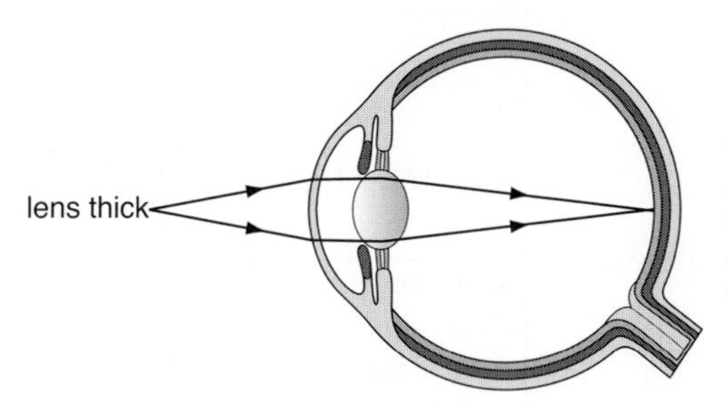
lens thick
light rays diverge; cornea refracts rays; lens is thicker as additional refraction is necessary to focus light on retina
eye focused on near object

The **ciliary muscle** is a ring of muscle that surrounds the lens. This muscle is attached to the lens by **suspensory ligaments** that resemble pieces of thread.

Figure 10.5 shows how the ciliary muscle controls the thickness of the lens.

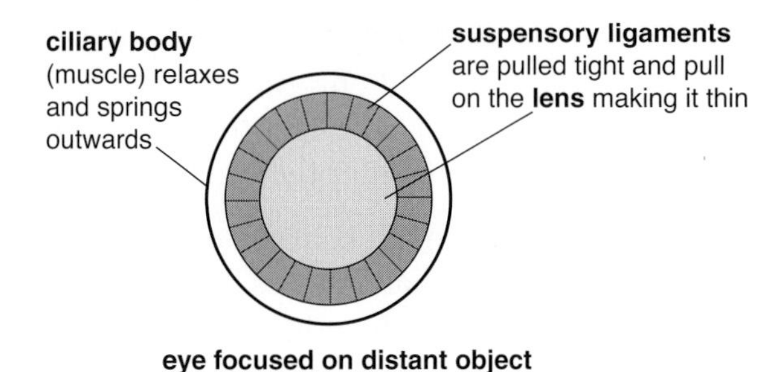
ciliary body
(muscle) relaxes
and springs
outwards
suspensory ligaments
are pulled tight and pull
on the lens making it thin
eye focused on distant object

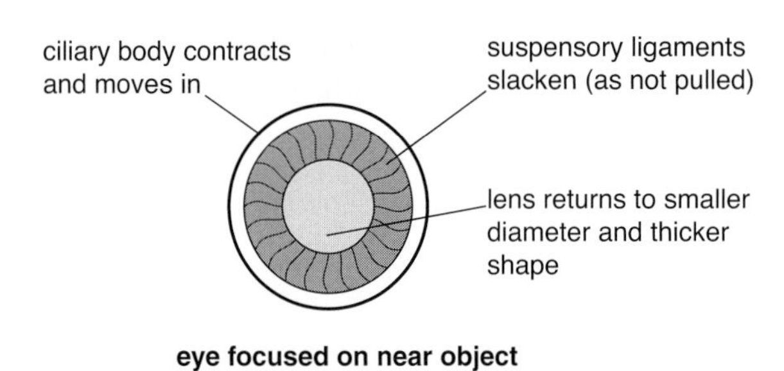
ciliary body contracts
and moves in
suspensory ligaments
slacken (as not pulled)
lens returns to smaller
diameter and thicker
shape
eye focused on near object

Figure 10.5 The action of ciliary muscle in the eye

The retina at the back of the eye carries two types of light-sensitive receptors. Their properties are listed in Table 10.2.

Table 10.2 Light-sensitive receptors

Light-sensitive receptors	Properties
rods	work in low light intensity but cannot distinguish between colours; lack precision vision; more numerous at outer edges of eye
cones	provide accurate colour vision; concentrated in centre of retina (fovea)

The eye is protected in the ways shown in Figure 10.6.

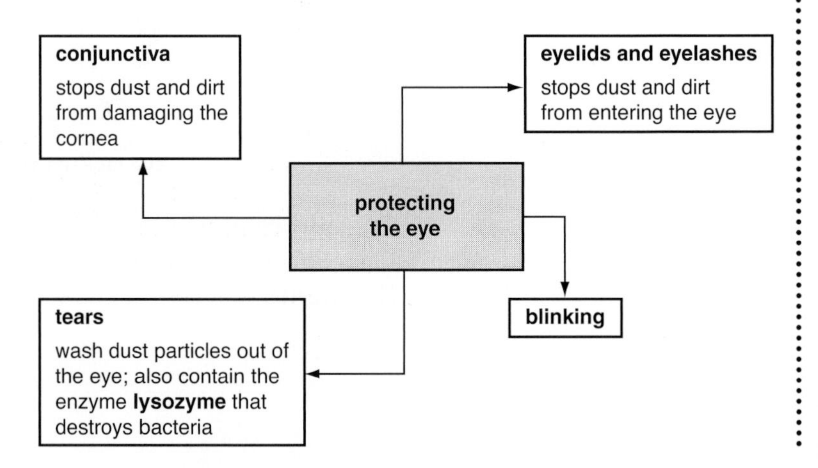
conjunctiva
stops dust and dirt
from damaging the
cornea
eyelids and eyelashes
stops dust and dirt
from entering the eye
protecting
the eye
blinking
tears
wash dust particles out of
the eye; also contain the
enzyme lysozyme that
destroys bacteria

Figure 10.6 Protecting the eye

Effectors in action – the elbow joint

The **biceps muscle** flexes (bends) the arm and the **triceps muscle** extends (straightens) the arm. The muscles are **effectors** and the elbow joint is the **pivot**. Figure 10.7 shows the process of flexing the arm.

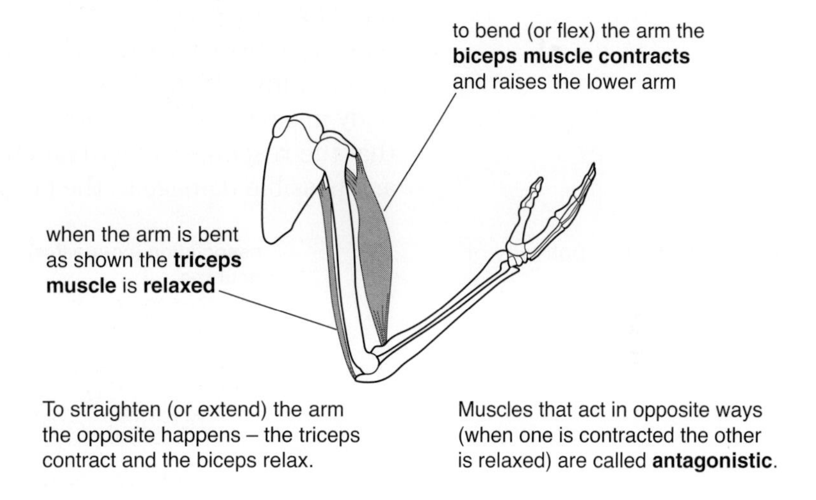
to bend (or flex) the arm the **biceps muscle contracts** and raises the lower arm
when the arm is bent as shown the **triceps muscle** is **relaxed**
To straighten (or extend) the arm the opposite happens – the triceps contract and the biceps relax.
Muscles that act in opposite ways (when one is contracted the other is relaxed) are called **antagonistic**.

Figure 10.7 Antagonistic muscles in the arm

The elbow joint in detail

The structure and function of the elbow joint are shown in Figure 10.8.

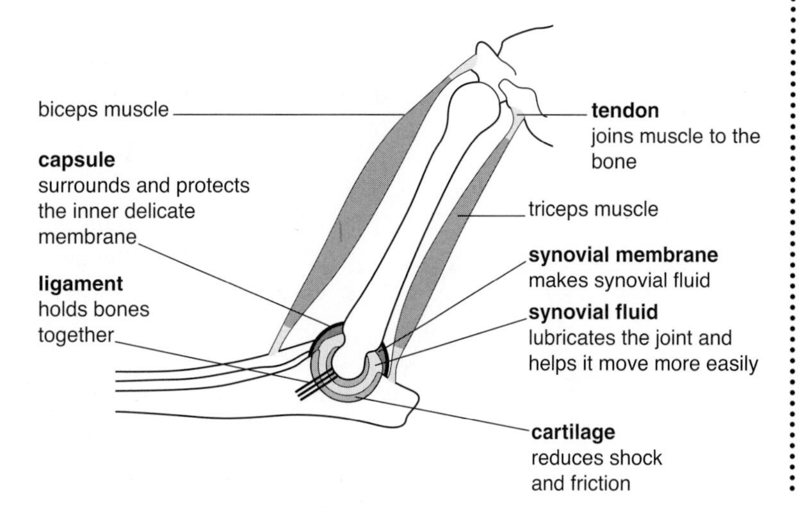
biceps muscle
capsule surrounds and protects the inner delicate membrane
ligament holds bones together
tendon joins muscle to the bone
triceps muscle
synovial membrane makes synovial fluid
synovial fluid lubricates the joint and helps it move more easily
cartilage reduces shock and friction

Figure 10.8 The elbow joint

Reflex actions

Reflex actions are very rapid reactions that are often of a protective nature. Examples include withdrawing the hand from a hot object, blinking and coughing. Figure 10.9 shows the pathway an impulse takes when a person holds their hand on a very hot object. Reflex actions are usually very rapid because they do not involve 'thinking time'. The nerve pathways involved are as short as possible and therefore may not involve the brain (depending on the parts of the body involved). The big advantage with a reflex action is that the response is rapid and therefore prevents or limits any possible damage to the body.

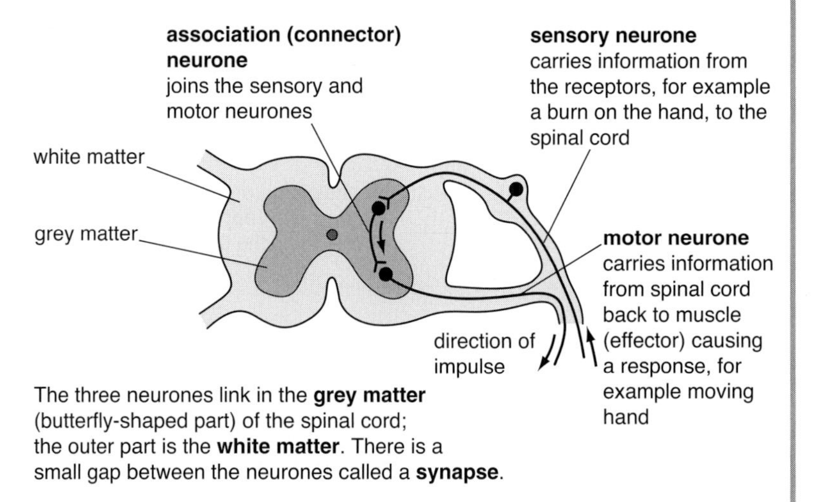
association (connector) neurone
joins the sensory and motor neurones
sensory neurone
carries information from the receptors, for example a burn on the hand, to the spinal cord
white matter
grey matter
motor neurone
carries information from spinal cord back to muscle (effector) causing a response, for example moving hand
direction of impulse
The three neurones link in the grey matter (butterfly-shaped part) of the spinal cord; the outer part is the white matter. There is a small gap between the neurones called a synapse.

Figure 10.9 The pathway of a reflex action

You are quite often asked to draw a reflex arc (or at least part of one) in an exam question. Very few candidates can draw a reflex arc accurately. Can you spot the three common mistakes in the attempt shown below?

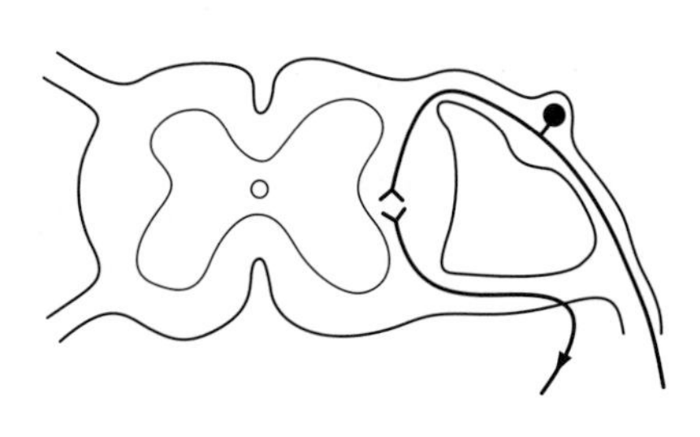

The mistakes are:

- neurones drawn in the white matter in the spinal cord – they should cross into the grey matter
- association (connector) neurone should not actually join with the other neurones – there should be a small gap at each end
- motor neurone drawn leaving the spinal column in the wrong place – it should leave along the same route as the sensory neurone.

The skin and temperature regulation

The skin has a very important role in keeping the body temperature at a constant 37 °C. There is always some heat loss from the skin but it can increase or decrease this loss depending on conditions. Figure 10.10 summarises how the skin increases heat loss in **hot conditions**.

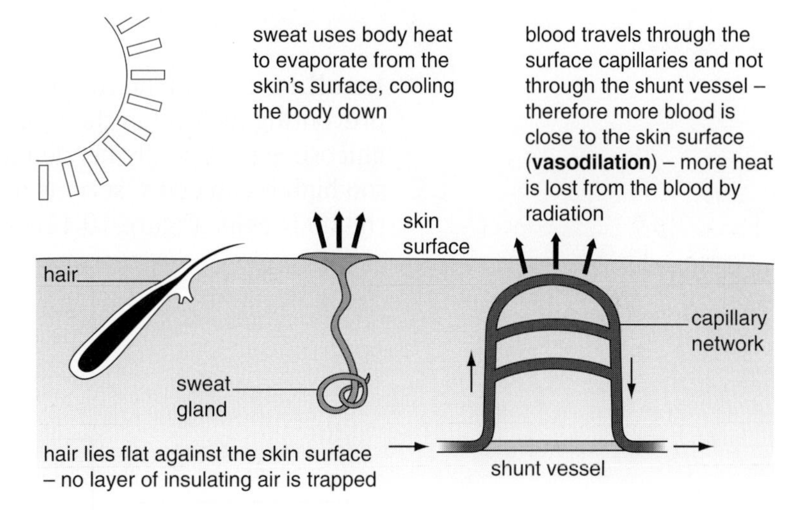
sweat uses body heat to evaporate from the skin's surface, cooling the body down
blood travels through the surface capillaries and not through the shunt vessel – therefore more blood is close to the skin surface (vasodilation) – more heat is lost from the blood by radiation
skin surface
hair
capillary network
sweat gland
hair lies flat against the skin surface – no layer of insulating air is trapped
shunt vessel

Figure 10.10 How the skin increases heat loss in hot conditions

In **cold conditions** the opposite responses happen in the skin:

- hairs rise to trap a layer of insulating air (in humans this is not effective over most of the body as the hair is not dense enough to trap the air – however raising of the hair can be recognised as 'goose pimples')
- sweat is no longer produced
- blood is directed through the shunt vessel (called **vasoconstriction**) and not through the surface capillaries – reducing heat loss by radiation as there is less blood near the skin's surface.

Also, in cold conditions muscles in the skin can contract involuntarily (**shiver**) to produce additional heat.

Question

1 Explain why the skin goes pale on a very cold day. *[3]*

Typical answer

1 Three of the following points for 3 marks: *[3]*

- vasoconstriction/the blood is directed through the shunt vessel/the blood does not go through the skin capillaries
- less blood reaches the skin surface
- less heat lost
- by radiation.

Hormones

Hormones are chemicals produced by special glands in the body that release the hormones directly into the blood. Hormones travel round in the blood and target certain organ(s) or parts of the body depending on the hormone concerned.

Insulin

Insulin is a hormone that regulates blood glucose level by preventing its level in the blood becoming too high. While glucose is continually needed for respiration, if its levels rise too high it can cause serious osmotic and other problems to the body cells. Figure 10.11 shows the action of insulin.

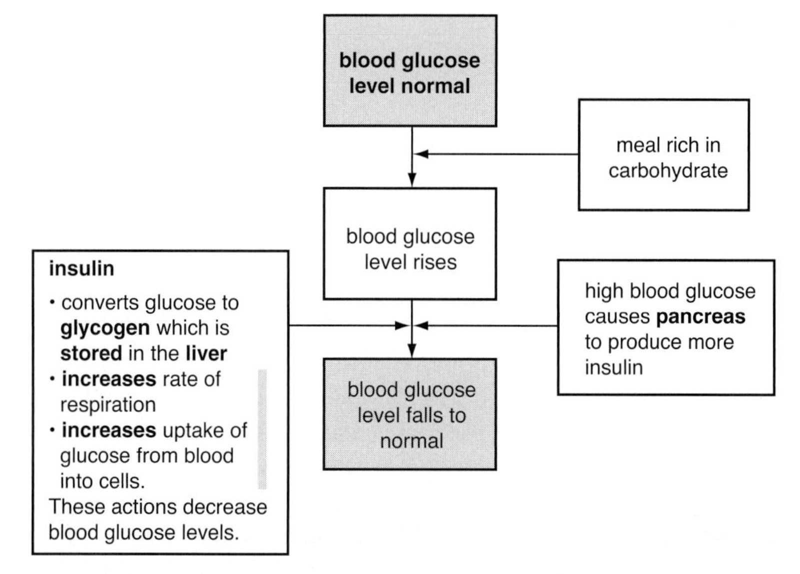
blood glucose level normal
meal rich in carbohydrate
blood glucose level rises
insulin
• converts glucose to glycogen which is stored in the liver
• increases rate of respiration
• increases uptake of glucose from blood into cells.
These actions decrease blood glucose levels.
high blood glucose causes pancreas to produce more insulin
blood glucose level falls to normal

Figure 10.11 The action of insulin

Figure 10.11 shows that insulin levels rise as blood glucose levels rise. Similarly as blood glucose levels fall this causes insulin levels to fall. This is important as if they did not then our glucose levels would be reduced far too much.

This is an example of a **feedback** mechanism where the results of hormone action can cause the reduction of the hormone production itself.

People who fail to produce enough insulin suffer from **diabetes**. Symptoms of diabetes include:

- sugar in the urine (if blood sugar levels are too high some sugar is excreted)
- extreme thirst (water is drawn into the concentrated blood from the surrounding body cells by osmosis making the cells dehydrated).

People with diabetes take insulin by injection. Insulin cannot be taken in tablet form as it would be digested in the stomach like any protein. It is important that the correct amount of insulin is taken to balance the person's food intake.

- If too little insulin is taken sugar levels may rise too much making the person feel unwell and risking complications.
- If too much insulin is taken and blood sugar levels fall too much a hypoglycaemic attack ('hypo') can result.

Question

1 Michael has diabetes. He ate his breakfast and injected his normal insulin dose. He ran the 500 metres to the bus stop instead of walking as normal as he was slightly late. After Michael arrived in school he felt faint and very unwell. He took a drink of a sugary drink and quickly felt much better. Explain why Michael felt unwell and then quickly recovered. *[4]*

Typical answer

1 The following four points for 4 marks:

- running for the bus used up more glucose than normal [1]
- Michael's blood glucose levels became very low [1]
- this caused him to feel faint and unwell [1]
- the sugary drink increased his blood glucose levels to normal. [1]

Adrenaline

Another hormone is **adrenaline**. It is known as the 'fight or flight' hormone as it prepares the body for action in times of danger or when excited. Some of the actions of adrenaline are summarised in Table 10.3.

Table 10.3 The actions of adrenaline

Response	Effect of response
glycogen converted to glucose in the liver	more glucose for more respiration and more energy
heart beats faster	more glucose and oxygen pumped to muscles for more respiration and more energy
bronchioles in lungs dilate	more oxygen is drawn into the lungs and more oxygen is available for more respiration and more energy
blood is diverted away from the skin and gut to the muscles	more glucose and oxygen pumped to muscles for more respiration and more energy; gives 'butterflies in the stomach' sensation

Some hormones are more long-term than the rapidly acting insulin and adrenaline. Examples are the hormones **testosterone** and **oestrogen** that are responsible for the development of secondary sexual characteristics during puberty. Their functions are shown in Table 10.4 on the next page.

Table 10.4 Functions of testosterone and oestrogen

Males (action of testosterone)	Females (action of oestrogen)
body hair and pubic hair develops	hair grows in pubic areas and armpits
sexual organs enlarge	sexual organs enlarge; breasts develop
voice deepens	menstruation begins
sexual awareness and drive increase	sexual awareness and drive increase

The effects of alcohol, drug and solvent abuse on the body

Figure 10.12 The effects of certain substances on the body

solvents
Include glue and lighter fluid. Can cause nausea and permanent brain, kidney and liver damage and death.

painkillers and antibiotics
Painkillers, e.g. penicillin, can cause harm if overused and even dependance. Antibiotics, if overused, can lead to the development of bacterial resistance.

stimulants
Examples include caffeine, amphetamines and cocaine. Can increase heart rate and awareness – can lead to addiction.

depressants
Examples include sleeping pills and 'downers'. Can cause drowsiness and psychological dependence.

alcohol
Results in inpaired judgement and lack of inhibition. Can lead to addiction and liver failure.

hallucinogens
Examples include ecstasy and LSD. Cause hallucinations/'mind altered states' and 'bad trips'.

As well as affecting the body, abuse of the substances shown in Figure 10.12 can affect **society** in many ways. These include:

- increased medical costs
- family and marriage problems
- violence and vandalism
- problems associated with school or work including increased absenteeism.

Exam questions

1 The diagram shows light from an object being focused by a human eye.

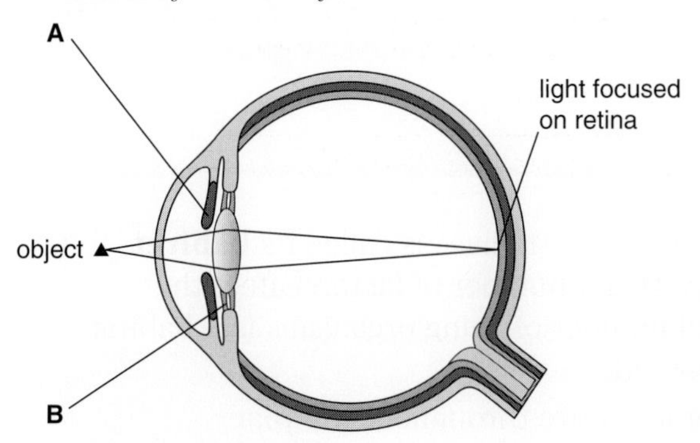
A
light focused
on retina
object
B

a Name parts **A** and **B**. *[2]*

b Describe how the image is focused on the retina and relayed to the brain. *[3]*
Quality of written communication will be assessed in this question. *[2]*

*Biology Paper 1 Foundation
June 2005*

2 This graph shows changes in blood glucose levels after a meal.

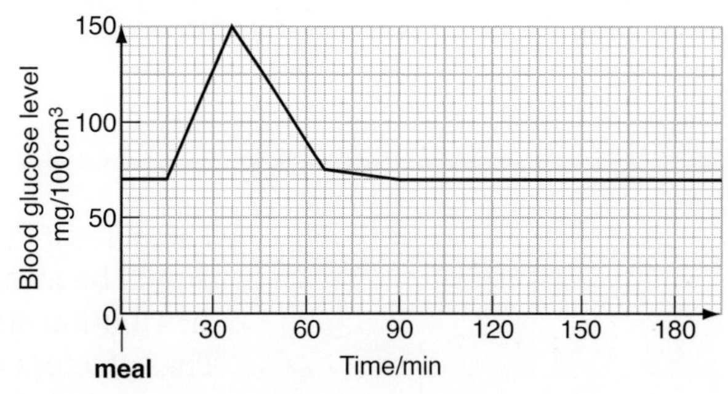
Blood glucose level
mg/100cm³
150
100
50
0
30
60
90
120
150
180
meal
Time/min

Give a **full** explanation for the shape of the graph. *[4]*

*Double Award (Modular)
End of Module Test Module A Higher
May 2005*

11 The transfer of energy and nutrients

The place a living organism lives is called its **habitat**. You should be aware that a number of factors affect the distribution and number of living organisms in a habitat. These factors include:

- change in temperature throughout the year
- availability of sunlight
- availability of water
- extent of cultivation – cultivated land tends to have fewer species present but more individuals of the crop plant(s) grown.

The first two factors in the above list have a very significant effect on habitats. Compare a hedgerow in January and June. The great increase in foliage in June is mainly due to higher temperatures and increased light levels.

Sampling

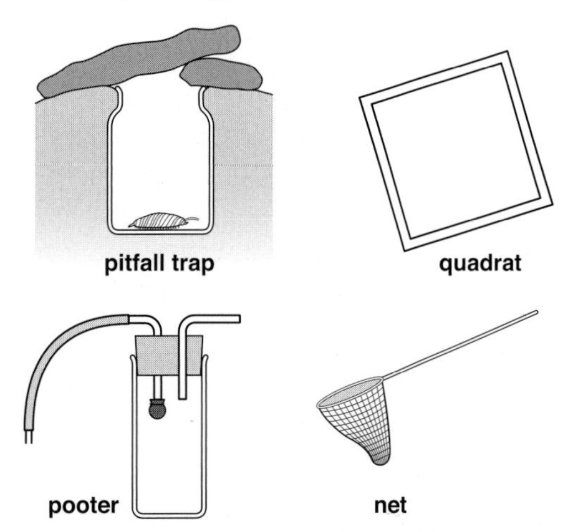

pitfall trap
quadrat
pooter
net

Figure 11.1 Some types of sampling apparatus

The apparatus shown in Figure 11.1 can be used to **sample** (obtain an estimate of the number) the organisms in a habitat in the following ways.

- **Pitfall trap:** a container is placed in a hole in the ground and a flat stone raised on smaller stones prevents the rain getting in. Suitable for ground-living animals such as beetles.
- **Quadrat:** a square frame that is placed over the ground to measure the distribution of plants or stationary animals, e.g. limpets. Usually a number of quadrats are used and an average obtained. The quadrats are thrown randomly over the area to be sampled. Plants that are difficult to measure as separate individuals, for example grasses, can be measured as percentage cover (percentage of quadrat covered by that plant to the nearest 10%).
- **Pooter:** a small tube that is used for sucking up small insects.
- **Net:** can be used for catching insects in long grass or water organisms in a stream or lake.

Transfer of energy

Food chains

Plants are the organisms that produce the energy that other living organisms depend on. Figure 11.2 outlines some of the key terms used in describing **food chains**.

Figure 11.2 A food chain – a chain of living organisms through which energy passes

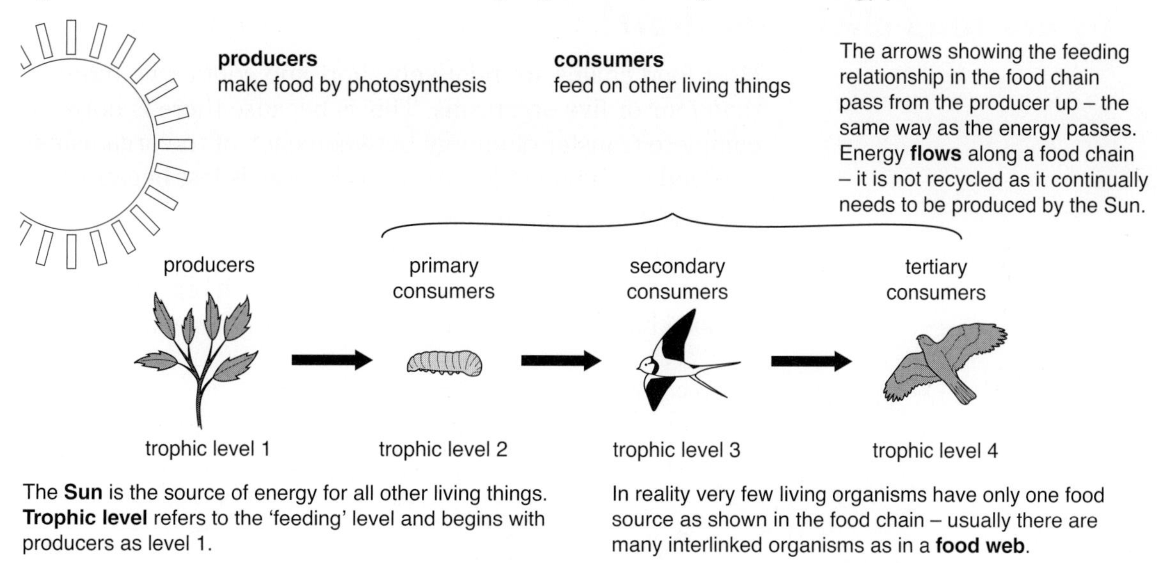
producers
make food by photosynthesis
consumers
feed on other living things
The arrows showing the feeding relationship in the food chain pass from the producer up – the same way as the energy passes. Energy flows along a food chain – it is not recycled as it continually needs to be produced by the Sun.
producers
primary consumers
secondary consumers
tertiary consumers
trophic level 1
trophic level 2
trophic level 3
trophic level 4
The Sun is the source of energy for all other living things. Trophic level refers to the 'feeding' level and begins with producers as level 1.
In reality very few living organisms have only one food source as shown in the food chain – usually there are many interlinked organisms as in a food web.

Pyramids of number and biomass

For a food chain or web to be sustainable there must be enough food available at any level for the organisms in the level above it. There are usually more producers than primary consumers and usually more primary consumers than secondary consumers and so on. This results in a **pyramid of numbers** as shown on the left in Figure 11.3.

Figure 11.3 Two types of pyramids of numbers

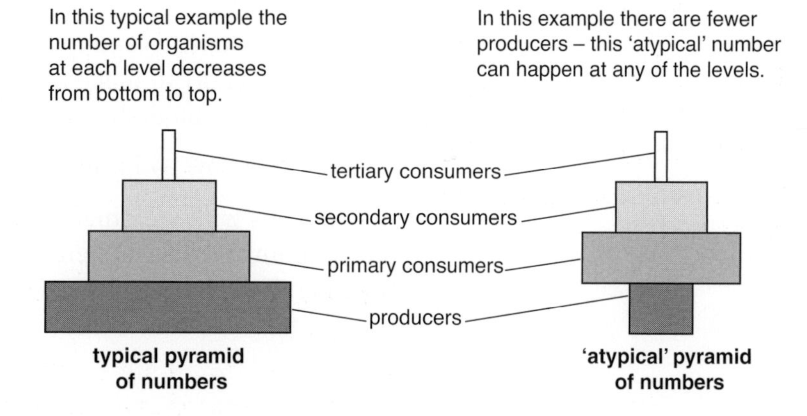
In this typical example the number of organisms at each level decreases from bottom to top.
In this example there are fewer producers – this 'atypical' number can happen at any of the levels.
tertiary consumers
secondary consumers
primary consumers
producers
typical pyramid of numbers
'atypical' pyramid of numbers

Sometimes the pyramid of numbers is not a pyramid as one very large organism such as a tree can act as a producer for many small primary consumers, for example insects (as shown on the right in Figure 11.3).

For this reason a **pyramid of biomass** that represents the biomass (mass of living material) can give a better representation – it is always a pyramid!

Why are food chains so short?

Most food chains are relatively short and contain no more than four or five organisms. This is because there is not a complete transfer of energy between each of the organisms involved as shown in Figure 11.4. Energy is lost because:

- not all the food is eaten
- not all the food is digested
- a lot of energy is lost in respiration by each organism in the food chain – this cannot be passed on to the next stage.

Figure 11.4 How energy is lost in a food chain

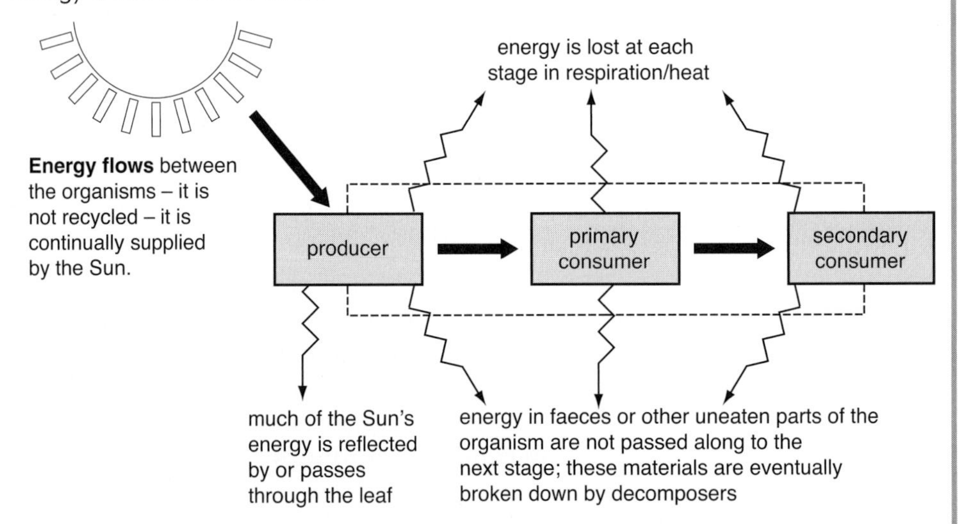
energy is lost at each stage in respiration/heat
Energy flows between the organisms – it is not recycled – it is continually supplied by the Sun.
producer
primary consumer
secondary consumer
much of the Sun's energy is reflected by or passes through the leaf
energy in faeces or other uneaten parts of the organism are not passed along to the next stage; these materials are eventually broken down by decomposers

The food chains involved in the feeding of humans are usually very short to make them more efficient. A typical example in Britain is the sequence:

grass → cow → human

In countries with very high populations there may be only one step involved as less energy is lost. For example rice is the main food in large areas of Asia.

Nutrient cycles

Nutrients such as carbon, nitrogen and other elements are essential to all living organisms. In a living system, or ecosystem, the nutrients tend to be recycled through the organisms involved. For this to happen, **fungi** and **bacteria** (**decomposers**), are involved in the process of decay and decomposition of dead material – otherwise the nutrients would get trapped in the bodies of dead plants and animals.

The carbon cycle

The **carbon cycle** is shown in Figure 11.5. It is a cycle that is of great interest in the world today. The increased burning of fossil fuels and the decrease in photosynthesis due to deforestation are leading to higher levels of atmospheric carbon dioxide which in turn lead to the **greenhouse effect** and **global warming** (the greenhouse effect and global warming are discussed on page 79).

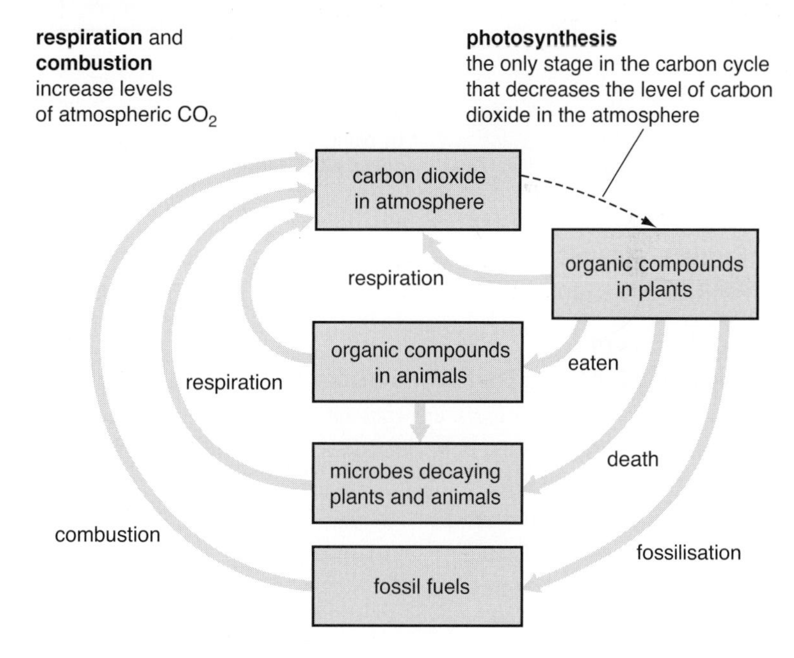
respiration and combustion increase levels of atmospheric CO_2
photosynthesis the only stage in the carbon cycle that decreases the level of carbon dioxide in the atmosphere
carbon dioxide in atmosphere
organic compounds in plants
respiration
organic compounds in animals
eaten
respiration
microbes decaying plants and animals
death
combustion
fossil fuels
fossilisation

Figure 11.5 The carbon cycle

The nitrogen cycle

The main phases of the nitrogen cycle are shown in Figure 11.6.

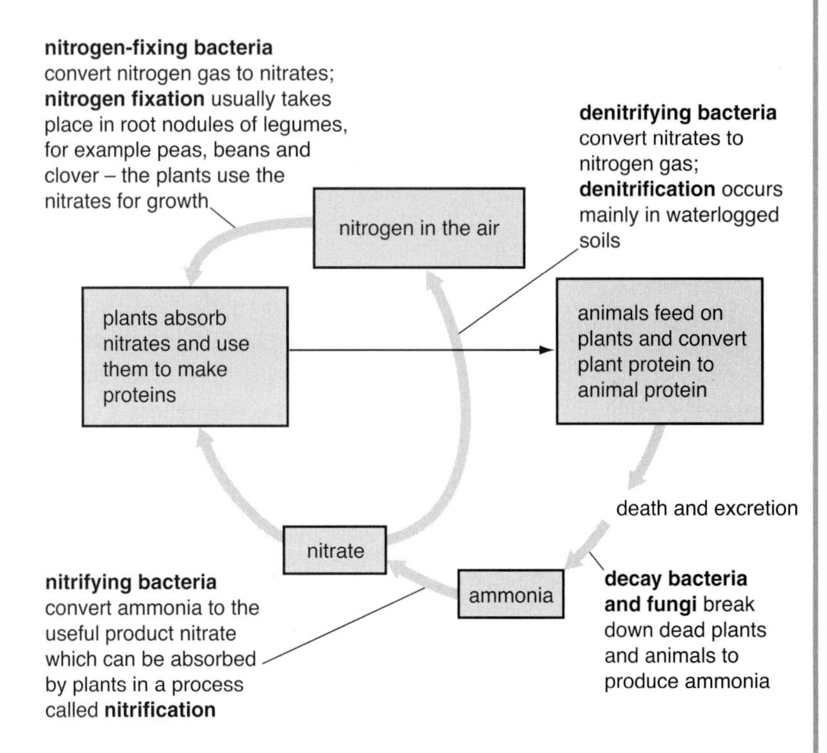
nitrogen-fixing bacteria convert nitrogen gas to nitrates; nitrogen fixation usually takes place in root nodules of legumes, for example peas, beans and clover – the plants use the nitrates for growth
nitrogen in the air
denitrifying bacteria convert nitrates to nitrogen gas; denitrification occurs mainly in waterlogged soils
plants absorb nitrates and use them to make proteins
animals feed on plants and convert plant protein to animal protein
death and excretion
nitrate
ammonia
decay bacteria and fungi break down dead plants and animals to produce ammonia
nitrifying bacteria convert ammonia to the useful product nitrate which can be absorbed by plants in a process called nitrification

Figure 11.6
The nitrogen cycle

Question

1 Farmers often plough legumes (plants that have root nodules containing nitrogen-fixing bacteria for example beans) back into the soil. Explain how this adds to the fertility of the soil. *[5]*

Typical answer

1 Five of the following points for 5 marks: *[5]*

- nitrogen-fixing bacteria convert nitrogen to nitrates
- protein in the plants is broken down by decay bacteria and fungi to ammonia
- nitrifying bacteria
- convert the ammonia to nitrates
- plants absorb nitrates
- nitrates used for amino acids/protein for growth.

Fertilisers

The removal of crops leads to a reduction in soil fertility because important elements are removed from the nutrient cycles. These elements can be replaced by **fertilisers**. Some examples of fertilisers and their functions are given in Table 11.1.

Table 11.1 Some examples of fertilisers

Type of fertiliser	Composition	Advantages	Disadvantages
manure/compost	plant and animal waste	improves soil quality; no cost; less soluble than artificial fertiliser; less likely to run-off into streams and cause pollution	difficult to store and spread; unknown nutrient composition
artificial fertiliser	industrially produced – usually rich in nitrogen, phosphorus and potassium (named 'NPK')	easier to store and spread; faster effect; known chemical composition	relatively high cost; soluble; easily washed away leading to pollution

Microbes and sewage disposal and composting

Sewage disposal

As with the decay and decomposition of organic material in nature, sewage systems use microbes to break down the organic material in sewage.

- **Aerobic bacteria:** digest the liquid waste in aeration tanks that maintain oxygen-rich conditions. The tanks contain stones covered with bacteria that digest the liquid sewage. After this stage disinfectant is added to destroy any harmful remains before the treated sewage is discharged into the sea.
- **Anaerobic bacteria:** break down solid waste. Gas given off from the process can be used as biogas and the solid remains can be used as fertiliser.

Composting

Microbes are also important in breaking down organic material in the compost heap as shown in Figure 11.7.

Figure 11.7 Decomposition in the compost heap

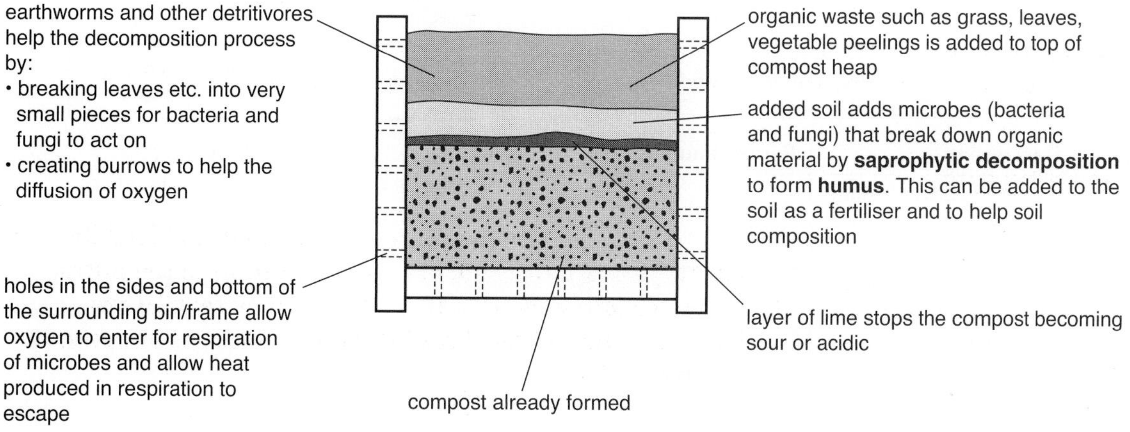

earthworms and other detritivores help the decomposition process by:
• breaking leaves etc. into very small pieces for bacteria and fungi to act on
• creating burrows to help the diffusion of oxygen

holes in the sides and bottom of the surrounding bin/frame allow oxygen to enter for respiration of microbes and allow heat produced in respiration to escape

compost already formed

organic waste such as grass, leaves, vegetable peelings is added to top of compost heap

added soil adds microbes (bacteria and fungi) that break down organic material by **saprophytic decomposition** to form **humus**. This can be added to the soil as a fertiliser and to help soil composition

layer of lime stops the compost becoming sour or acidic

Exam question

1 The diagram below shows a food web for heath land.

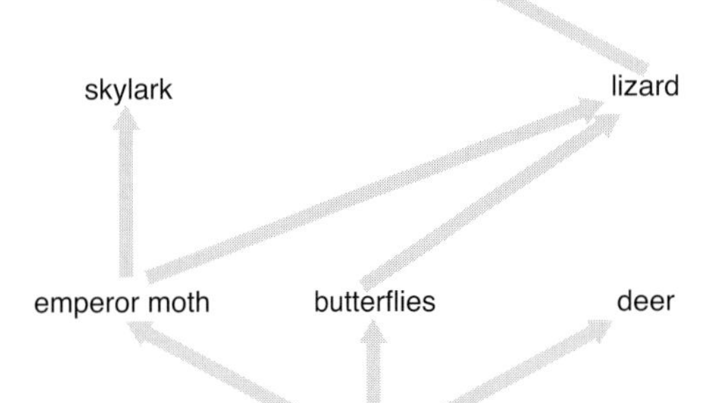
adder
skylark
lizard
emperor moth
butterflies
deer
heather plants

a i What is the energy source for a food web? *[1]*

ii Draw a food chain containing four organisms using only the information in the food web. *[2]*

iii Name a secondary consumer in this food web. *[1]*

b i If the number of skylarks suddenly decreases what effect will this have on the number of moths? Explain your answer. *[2]*

ii State **two** factors (other than predation) that may affect the population growth of the moths. *[2]*

Quality of written communication will be assessed in this question. *[2]*

c The diagrams represent pyramids of numbers for food chains.

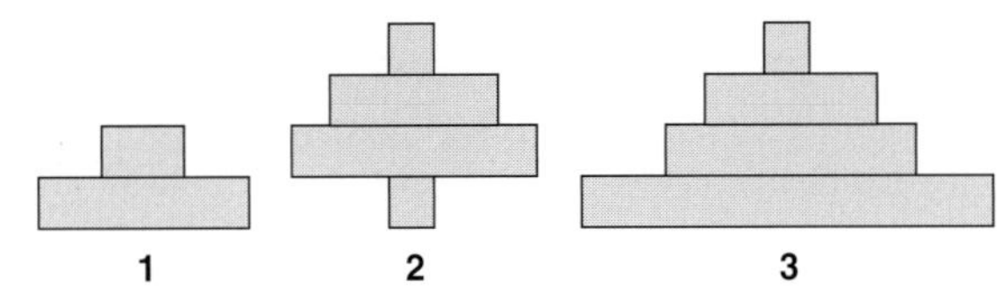
1
2
3

Copy and complete the table below by matching the number of the pyramid above with the correct description given in the table. *[2]*

Description	Pyramid number
an adder eats lizards which in turn eat moths which feed on heather plants	
a hawk eats skylarks which eat caterpillars which eat leaves of an oak tree	
deer eat grass	

d Beetles and butterflies are found on the heath land.
The diagram shows the apparatus which can be used to trap beetles.

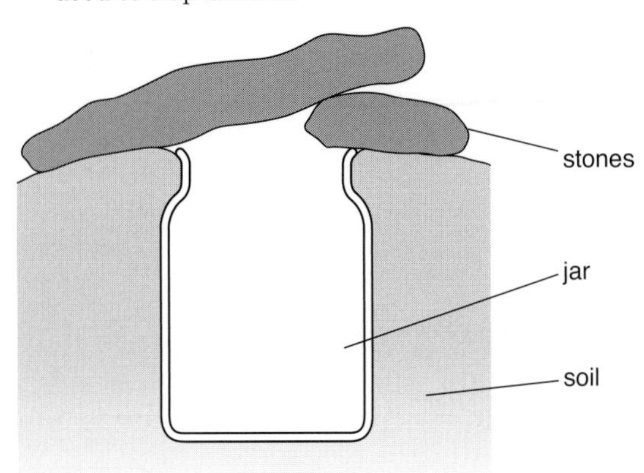
stones
jar
soil

i Name this apparatus. *[1]*

ii Why can this apparatus not be used to trap butterflies? *[1]*

e The diagram shows the carbon cycle.

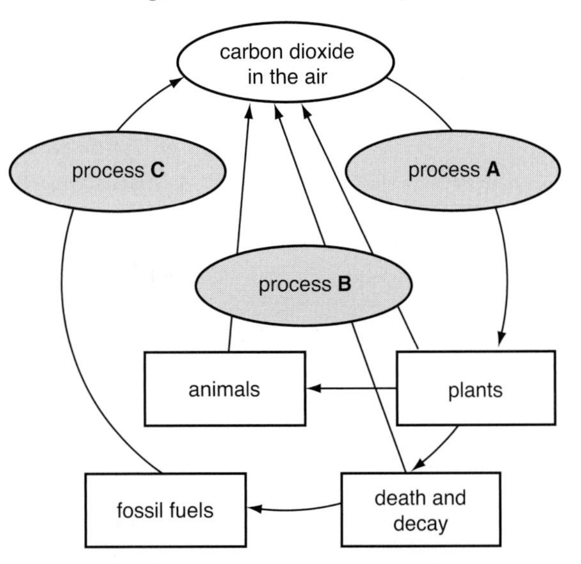
carbon dioxide in the air
process C
process A
process B
animals
plants
fossil fuels
death and decay

i Name the processes **A**, **B** and **C**. *[3]*

ii Why is the return of carbon dioxide to the air so important to animals? *[1]*

iii Name **two** types of decomposers. *[2]*

Double Award (Modular)
Paper 1 Foundation
June 2006

12

Pollution and conservation

Pollution is the addition of harmful substances to the environment. Humans are almost entirely responsible for the pollution that affects the planet.

Air pollution

The main types of air pollution and possible remedial actions are listed in Table 12.1.

Table 12.1 The main types of air pollution and ways of reducing them

Pollutant	How pollution is caused	Effect	Method of reducing pollution
soot	burning fossil fuels	covers leaves of plants reducing photosynthesis; blocks stomata reducing gas exchange	smokeless fuels; alternative fuels such as solar or wind power
sulphur dioxide	burning fossil fuels, particularly in power stations	sulphur dioxide combines with water in the atmosphere to form acid rain which kills trees and fish	filters in power stations; alternative fuels; catalytic converters
carbon monoxide	produced in car exhausts	combines with haemoglobin to reduce carriage of oxygen in blood	catalytic converters
lead	previously used as additive in petrol and in paint; still a problem in underdeveloped countries	brain damage in children	unleaded petrol; lead-free paint

Land pollution

We produce both **biodegradable** and **non-biodegradable** waste.

- Biodegradable waste can be broken down by microbes and includes vegetable waste and paper.
- Non-biodegradable waste includes plastic that does not naturally break down and so accumulates over time.

Landfill or incineration?

Rubbish can be either added to landfill sites or incinerated (burned). The advantages and disadvantages of these methods of rubbish disposal are shown in Table 12.2.

Table 12.2 Rubbish disposal

Method of disposal	Advantage	Disadvantage
landfill	less air pollution	shortage of land; unsightly; attracts vermin
incineration	can generate power as rubbish is burned; does not use up land	expensive to build; can pollute the atmosphere with carbon dioxide therefore contributing to global warming

Recycling paper

The advantages of recycling paper are:

- reduction in deforestation
- less carbon dioxide is produced through the burning of trees (parts not used in making paper)
- helps to maintain habitats and biodiversity
- maintains soil quality through decreasing soil erosion in forest areas.

The disadvantages include:

- extra expense in producing paper
- paper is not usually of as high quality.

Water pollution

Water pollution can arise for a number of reasons:

- sewage
- cattle slurry
- silage effluent
- fertiliser run-off.

Each of these can enrich the water to such an extent that **eutrophication** results.

Eutrophication

The steps in eutrophication are shown in Figure 12.1.

Figure 12.1 Eutrophication

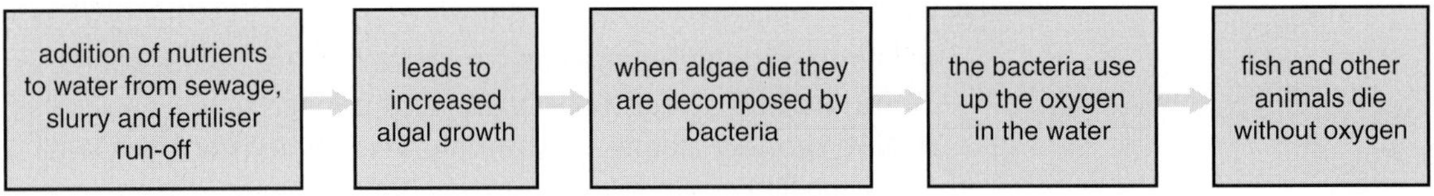

addition of nutrients to water from sewage, slurry and fertiliser run-off → leads to increased algal growth → when algae die they are decomposed by bacteria → the bacteria use up the oxygen in the water → fish and other animals die without oxygen

A similar process can happen when hot water enters waterways from **industrial cooling processes**. The effluent contains much less oxygen than normal water and the extra warmth can also cause increased growth of algae.

Reducing water pollution

Water pollution can be reduced in the following ways.

- More careful storage and use or disposal of fertiliser, slurry and silage effluent.
- Sewage treatment is becoming more effective at reducing all the harmful materials before the treated sewage enters the waterways. It is more effective now at reducing the chemicals that can cause eutrophication.

Conservation

This is the process of conserving the planet and its resources for future generations. **Biodiversity** describes the range of species and habitats that exist. Some examples of the threat to our biodiversity and measures taken to conserve it are listed below.

- **Deforestation:** the removal of trees for wood or to create land for agriculture or housing. This reduces biodiversity, produces more carbon dioxide and leads to soil erosion and possibly flooding. Conservation measures include:
  reafforestation: replacing trees in woodland areas, and **afforestation:** creating new forests in areas where they did not previously exist.
- **Monoculture:** this is the growing of a single type of crop over large areas, for example maize. This decreases biodiversity and reduces soil fertility as the same crop uses the same minerals year after year. Conservation measures are crop rotation and allowing some areas to remain natural.

Conservation of fish stocks

Many fish populations including the North Sea herring population have been in sharp decline as a result of over-fishing. Measures to increase stocks again include the following.

- Setting of **quotas:** limiting the number of fish that can be caught and also times when fishing can take place.
- Using **larger mesh sizes:** so that smaller fish can escape and breed.
- **Decommissioning boats:** to reduce the number of fishing vessels.
- Setting up **sanctuaries:** where fishing is banned.

Competition from non-native species

An example of competition from non-native species is the introduction of the grey squirrel into Britain from America. As the grey squirrel is able to feed on a wider range of foods and produces more offspring than the native red squirrel, it has eliminated the red squirrel from much of Britain. Conservation measures include controlling the numbers of grey squirrels in selected sites and special feeding systems that only the red squirrels can gain access to.

The overuse of **herbicides** (weedkillers) and **pesticides** (kill insect pests) has reduced biodiversity including the number of birds through destroying their food sources. It is important that herbicide and pesticide use is carefully controlled to prevent further decline in bird populations.

DDT is a persistent pesticide that is now banned in much of the developing world. It cannot be broken down or excreted and so accumulates in organisms at the top of the food chain and kills them. An example is predatory birds whose populations were dying out at the height of DDT use.

However, DDT is still used in some developing countries to attempt to combat the mosquitoes that cause malaria as it is cheap and reliable.

Measures such as those given above help to conserve biodiversity and variation and preserve **endangered species**. These are species that have low numbers and are at risk of becoming extinct, for example the red squirrel and North Sea herring.

The changing biosphere and the need for international action

Major international conferences such as Kyoto and Johannesburg (2002) have tried to make the world aware of some of the major environmental issues that affect the planet. In addition many of these environmental issues affect many or all countries. They include the following.

- **Acid rain:** occurs when sulphur and nitrogen oxides combine with atmospheric water. It kills trees by creating a more acidic soil that affects microbial activity in producing nutrients. Fish in lakes are killed through aluminium poisoning that is released from the surrounding acidic soils. A major problem has been that the factories producing the acid rain may be in a different country from that affected by it. However, acid rain is becoming less of a problem today and many affected areas are recovering through effective filters in power stations and the use of alternative fuels.

- **The greenhouse effect and global warming:** increasing levels of atmospheric carbon dioxide (due to increased burning of fossil fuels and deforestation) are causing the atmosphere to warm up as shown in Figure 12.2.

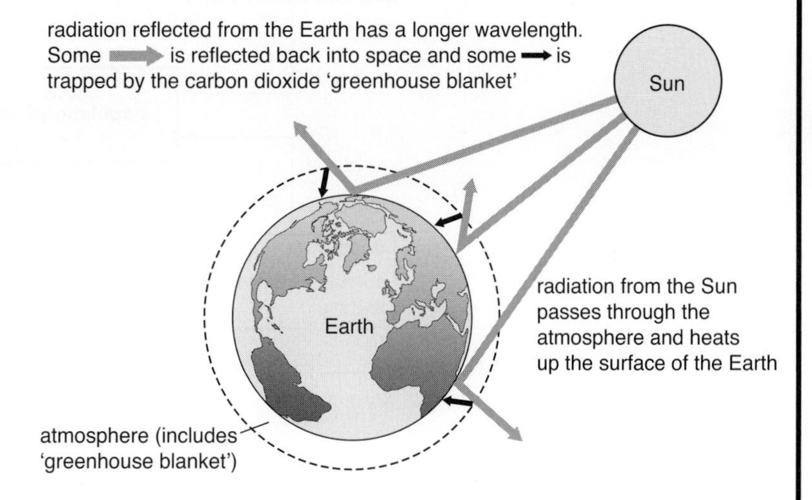
radiation reflected from the Earth has a longer wavelength. Some is reflected back into space and some is trapped by the carbon dioxide 'greenhouse blanket'
Sun
Earth
radiation from the Sun passes through the atmosphere and heats up the surface of the Earth
atmosphere (includes 'greenhouse blanket')

Figure 12.2 The greenhouse effect and global warming

Global warming is producing the following effects:

- melting of the polar ice caps leading to a rise in sea levels
- changing weather patterns with more extreme weather – hotter summers, more frequent and stronger storms, droughts
- habitat change.

The major political nations are beginning to accept that global warming is a major issue and steps are being taken to reduce the build up of carbon dioxide in the atmosphere. These measures include the development of alternative fuels and increased recycling measures.

The ozone layer

Ozone is found in the upper atmosphere. It is a very important gas as it absorbs ultraviolet light coming from the Sun and prevents too much of it reaching the Earth's surface. It is now known that CFCs (chemicals found in aerosols and refrigerators) have built up in the atmosphere and may be responsible for reducing the thickness of the ozone layer.

Measures to reduce the thinning of the ozone layer include substitutes for CFCs and the proper disposal of refrigerators.

Populations

The **population** of a species is the total number of that species in an area. Figure 12.3 outlines the factors that can affect a population.

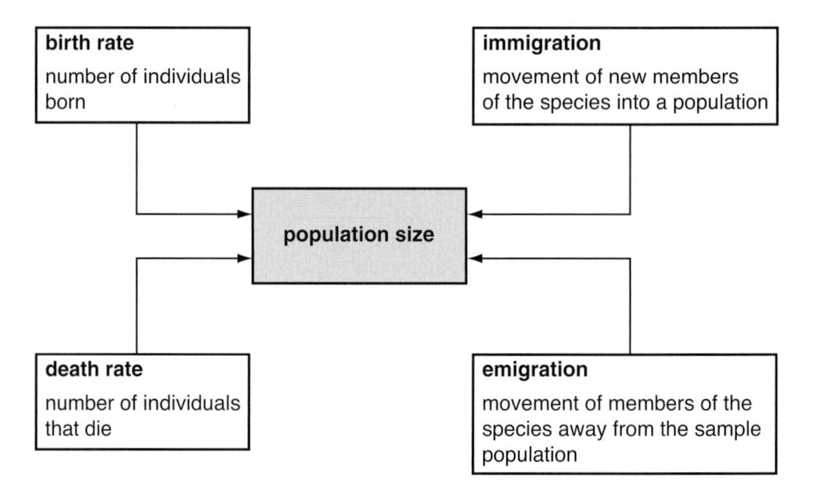
birth rate
number of individuals born
immigration
movement of new members of the species into a population
population size
death rate
number of individuals that die
emigration
movement of members of the species away from the sample population

Figure 12.3 The factors affecting the size of a population

The change in a population can be represented by:

birth rate + immigration − (death rate + emigration)

When a **food supply** is readily available populations tend to grow rapidly but where **predation** or **disease** is common populations grow much more slowly or may even decrease.

Note: Most questions on populations do not involve immigration or emigration. If there is no migration, it is important to know that if there is:

- no change, then birth rate = death rate
- a population increase, then birth rate > death rate
- a population decrease, then birth rate < death rate.

The human population is increasing rapidly in part due to:

- increase in **food supply** for many areas of the world
- improvement in **sanitation** which reduces illness and death due to infection
- improvement in **medical care** such as the development of vaccines and antibiotics.

The rate of growth of human population is concerning due to the pressures it is putting on the Earth's resources. Some countries place a limit on the number of children parents can have and in other countries the use of contraception is encouraged to limit family size.

Exam questions

1 a i Give **three** ways that deforestation can damage the environment. *[3]*

ii Give **one** way that the damage caused by deforestation can be reversed. *[1]*

b If fertiliser runs off the land into a river it causes a process called eutrophication.
The diagram shows the stages of eutrophication. Answer the questions beside the different stages.

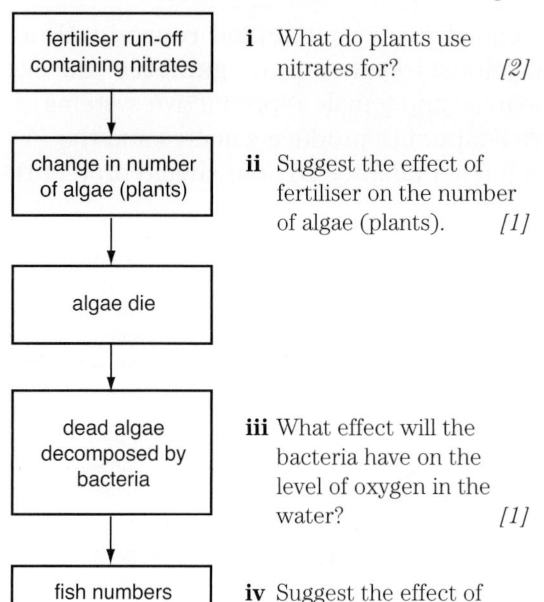
fertiliser run-off containing nitrates
change in number of algae (plants)
algae die
dead algae decomposed by bacteria
fish numbers affected

i What do plants use nitrates for? *[2]*

ii Suggest the effect of fertiliser on the number of algae (plants). *[1]*

iii What effect will the bacteria have on the level of oxygen in the water? *[1]*

iv Suggest the effect of eutrophication on the number of fish. *[1]*

c The presence of small animals can be used to indicate pollution levels in the river.
The table shows some examples.

Small animal	Pollution level
rat-tailed maggot sludge worm	high
blood worm water louse	medium
stonefly nymph mayfly nymph	low

Water samples were taken from three locations along the river. The three locations were:

- just after the fertiliser run-off which was near the source of the river
- halfway down the river
- far down the river near mouth of river.

Sample 1 contained stonefly nymphs and mayfly nymphs.
Sample 2 contained rat-tailed maggots and sludge worms.

i Suggest the location from which each sample was taken. *[2]*

ii Name **two** substances, other than fertiliser, that could cause eutrophication in the river. *[2]*

Double Award (Modular)
Paper 1 Foundation
June 2005

2 The table shows number of herring caught between the years 1987 and 1991.

	Year				
	1987	**1988**	**1989**	**1990**	**1991**
number of herring caught per 1000 tonnes	1305	1401	1356	1214	1110

a Which year had the lowest catch? *[1]*

b Explain why the herring numbers are decreasing. *[2]*

One way to reduce the decline in herring population is to set a quota.

c What is meant by a **quota**? *[1]*

d Describe **two** other ways some governments are trying to prevent the extinction of the herring population. *[2]*

Biology Paper 1 Higher
June 2004

13

Human reproduction

Humans (and mammals) carry out **sexual reproduction** that involves the joining together of two **gametes** (the egg and sperm). The male and female reproductive systems (Figure 13.1) are adapted to produce gametes and the female system is further adapted to nourish and protect the developing baby.

Figure 13.1 The male and female reproductive systems

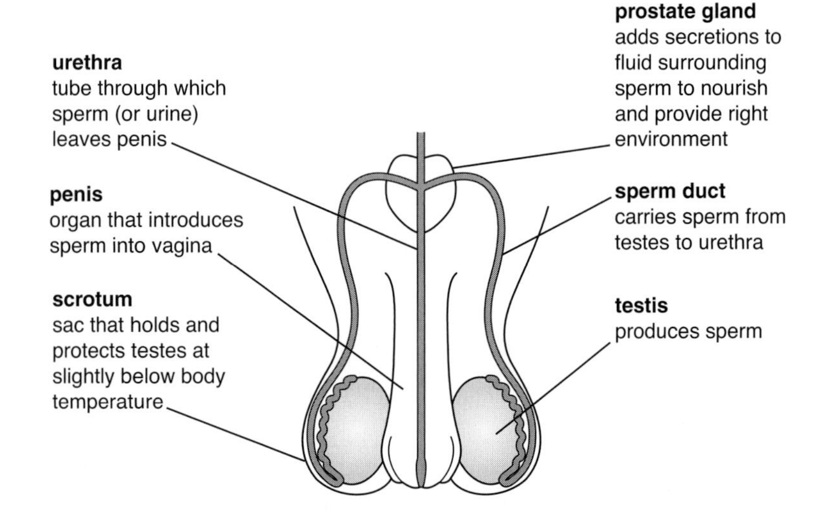
urethra
tube through which sperm (or urine) leaves penis
penis
organ that introduces sperm into vagina
scrotum
sac that holds and protects testes at slightly below body temperature
prostate gland
adds secretions to fluid surrounding sperm to nourish and provide right environment
sperm duct
carries sperm from testes to urethra
testis
produces sperm

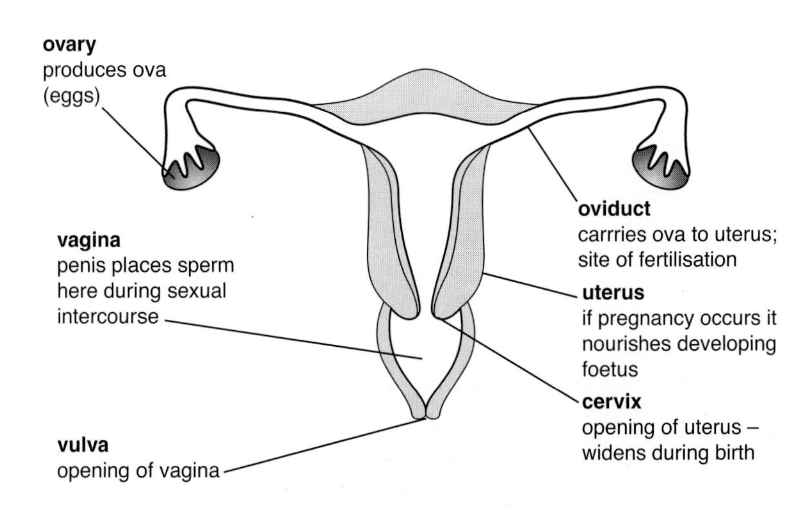
ovary
produces ova (eggs)
vagina
penis places sperm here during sexual intercourse
vulva
opening of vagina
oviduct
carrries ova to uterus; site of fertilisation
uterus
if pregnancy occurs it nourishes developing foetus
cervix
opening of uterus – widens during birth

Fertilisation and embryo development

The sperm and egg (each with 23 chromosomes) fuse in the oviduct to form the **zygote** with 46 chromosomes. The zygote then divides by mitosis to form a ball of cells that **implants** in the uterus lining. Figure 13.2 shows a foetus in the uterus and the structures that protect and nourish it.

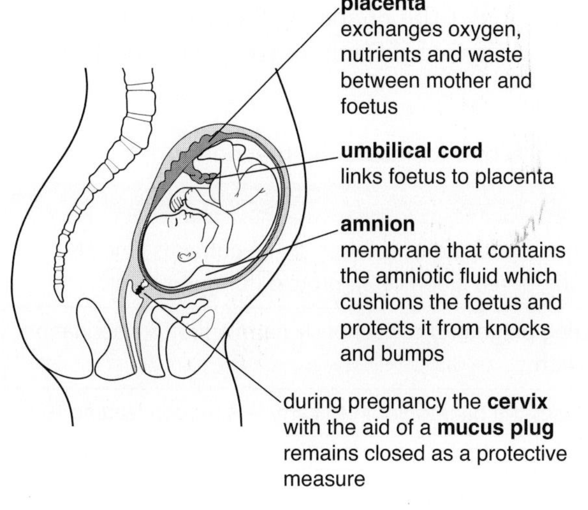
placenta
exchanges oxygen, nutrients and waste between mother and foetus
umbilical cord
links foetus to placenta
amnion
membrane that contains the amniotic fluid which cushions the foetus and protects it from knocks and bumps
during pregnancy the **cervix** with the aid of a **mucus plug** remains closed as a protective measure

Figure 13.2 The foetus in the uterus and the surrounding protective structures

Birth

Just before birth the baby turns round so that its head is at the cervix. Birth involves the following processes:

- uterus muscles contract to begin pushing the baby out
- mucus plug dissolves
- cervix dilates (widens)
- amnion ruptures to release amniotic fluid ('breaking of the waters')
- following birth the placenta (afterbirth) is passed out.

The role of the placenta

The placenta is the region where the mother's blood contacts the foetal blood as shown in Figure 13.3.

Figure 13.3 The functions of the placenta

placenta
very rich in maternal blood vessels; mother's blood is rich in oxygen and other nutrients

uterus wall

umbilical cord
contains:
- **umbilical artery** carries urea, carbon dioxide and other wastes back to the mother.
- **umbilical vein** carries oxygen, glucose, amino acids and other nutrients from the mother to the foetus

amnion
contains amniotic fluid

boundary between maternal blood and foetal blood

The blood systems are not joined but are close together and separated by thin membranes to allow diffusion of gases and nutrients to take place in either direction.
The 'finger-like' boundary increases the surface area for diffusion. The blood systems cannot be joined as the mother and foetus may be of different blood groups.

Factors that affect pregnancy

Certain factors can affect the chances of a pregnant women giving birth to a healthy baby. Some of these are shown in Table 13.1.

Table 13.1 Some of the factors that can affect the health of a foetus during pregnancy

Factor	Effect
diet	a maternal balanced diet is essential to ensure that a foetus receives all the nutrients it needs including calcium (for teeth and bones); iron (for red blood cells); protein (for growth), etc.
rubella	rubella (German measles) if contracted during pregnancy can seriously harm a foetus; vaccination programmes reduce the possibility of infection
smoking	carbon monoxide from cigarette smoke causes the haemoglobin to carry less oxygen leading to lower birth weights
alcohol	if taken in excess can harm a foetus and lead to miscarriage
drugs	can seriously damage a foetus; babies can be born who are dependent on the drugs used by the mother

Factors that affect the development of infants

Certain factors can affect the development of infants. Some of these are shown in Table 13.2.

Table 13.2 Some of the factors that can affect the health of an infant

Factor	Effect
breastfeeding	breast milk contains antibodies from the mother and also has correct proportions of nutrients to meet the baby's needs
balanced diet	very important due to on-going development and growth; same essential nutrients as listed in Table 13.1
immunisation programme	immunisation programmes are in place to protect against potentially harmful diseases such as measles; mumps; rubella; tetanus; polio
parental care and loving environment	necessary to protect the child and to allow for emotional growth

Puberty

Puberty is the stage when the body is prepared for reproduction – physically and emotionally. The changes associated with puberty (secondary sexual characteristics) are listed in Chapter 10.

Menstruation

Menstruation occurs in females from puberty until the end of reproductive life (usually sometime in the fifties). The purpose of menstruation is to prepare the female reproductive system for pregnancy by controlling the monthly release of an egg and renewing and replacing the uterine lining. Menstruation is controlled by the female hormones. Table 13.3 outlines the monthly menstrual cycle.

Table 13.3 The menstrual cycle

Day (approximately)	What happens
1–5	uterine lining breaks down and passes out of body (menstruation)
6–12	uterine lining builds up in preparation for implantation should pregnancy result
13–15	an egg is released from an ovary (ovulation)
16–28	if an egg is not fertilised there is no further development of the uterine lining; if there is a pregnancy, placenta and associated structures develop

Responsible sexual behaviour

Sexually transmitted diseases

Responsible sexual behaviour is necessary to avoid transmission of sexually transmitted diseases and to prevent unplanned pregnancy.

Common sexually transmitted diseases include the following.

- **Gonorrhoea:** a **bacterial** infection that is passed during **sexual contact** and can be treated with **antibiotics**. It can be avoided by limiting the number of sexual partners and using a condom.
- **AIDS:** a **viral** infection that is spread by the **exchange of body fluids** (mainly during sexual intercourse) but also in infected blood and drug addicts sharing needles. It is usually fatal but its progression can be slowed down by anti-viral drugs. Chances of contracting AIDS can be reduced by limiting the number of sexual partners and using a condom.

Types of contraception

Pregnancy can be prevented (or its possibility reduced) by using **contraception**. Some different types of contraception are listed in Table 13.4.

Table 13.4 Some different types of contraception and their reliability

Type	Example/ description	Reliability	Advantages	Disadvantages
natural	avoid sex close to time of ovulation	unreliable	no chemicals involved; favoured by some religions	very unreliable; may be difficult to determine time of ovulation
mechanical	condom prevents sperm from entering female	fairly reliable	no chemicals; easily obtained	interferes with spontaneity of intercourse; unreliable if not used properly
mechanical	diaphragm/cap prevents sperm entering cervix	fairly reliable	can be put in and removed well before and after sexual intercourse	needs to be inserted well before intercourse; should be used with a spermicide spray
mechanical	IUD (intrauterine device) restricts sperm movement through uterus and prevents implantation	very reliable	no chemicals; long term	can cause heavy bleeding; increased possibility of infection
chemical	pill prevents eggs from being released	very reliable	reliability; does not interfere with sexual intercourse	side-effects of weight gain and blood pressure; only obtained from doctor or clinic
surgical	female or male sterilisation by cutting oviducts or sperm ducts respectively	virtually 100% reliable as prevents sperm and egg making contact	reliable	very difficult to reverse

Fertility problems and their treatment

Some people have problems (fertility problems) that prevent them becoming pregnant. Some of the reasons are:

- failure of ovary to produce ova
- oviducts may be blocked or twisted, possibly due to infection

- lining of the uterus does not develop properly to enable implantation to occur
- vagina may be hostile to sperm entering, for example the lining may be too thick or too acidic
- males may not produce enough or healthy sperm; sperm numbers can be affected by smoking or taking alcohol in excess
- impotence.

Treatments for infertility can include those shown in Figure 13.4.

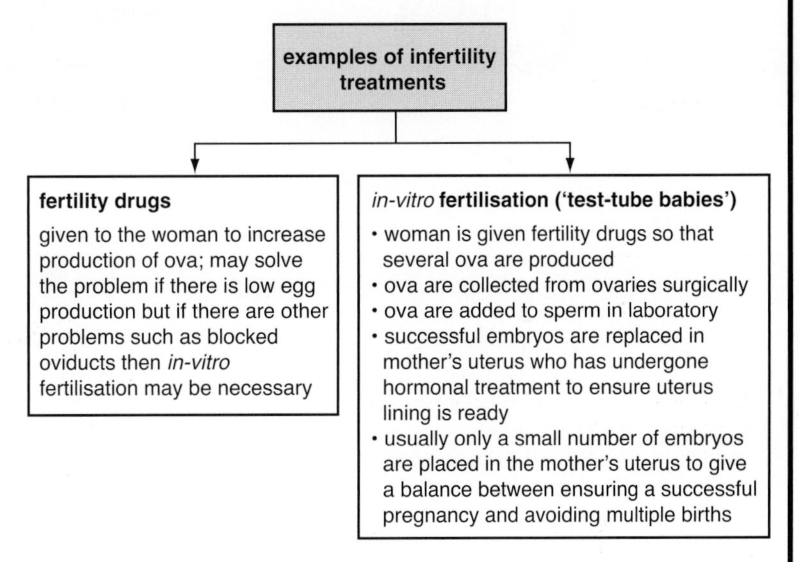
examples of infertility treatments
fertility drugs
given to the woman to increase production of ova; may solve the problem if there is low egg production but if there are other problems such as blocked oviducts then in-vitro fertilisation may be necessary
in-vitro fertilisation ('test-tube babies')
• woman is given fertility drugs so that several ova are produced
• ova are collected from ovaries surgically
• ova are added to sperm in laboratory
• successful embryos are replaced in mother's uterus who has undergone hormonal treatment to ensure uterus lining is ready
• usually only a small number of embryos are placed in the mother's uterus to give a balance between ensuring a successful pregnancy and avoiding multiple births

Figure 13.4 Some treatments for infertility

Reproductive techniques in farming

Similar reproductive technology can be used for commercial reasons with livestock.

Again hormones can be used to develop many ova in a cow with desirable characteristics such as high milk yield. The cow can be artificially inseminated with sperm from a high quality bull and multiple embryos may begin to develop. After a few weeks these can be washed out of the pregnant cow and transferred to other 'surrogate' cows. The 'surrogate' mothers are treated with hormones to ensure that the uterine lining allows an embryo to implant.

Artificial insemination has the advantage in ensuring that high quality offspring will result. In addition if several cows are artificially inseminated together then all the calves will be born at around the same time.

Exam questions

1 The diagrams show the male and female reproductive systems.

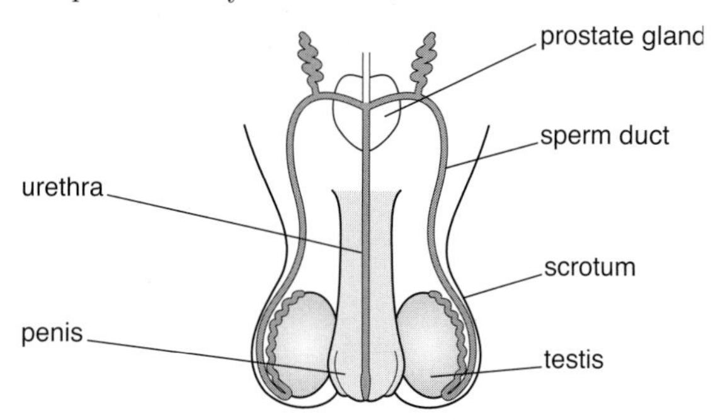
prostate gland
sperm duct
urethra
scrotum
penis
testis

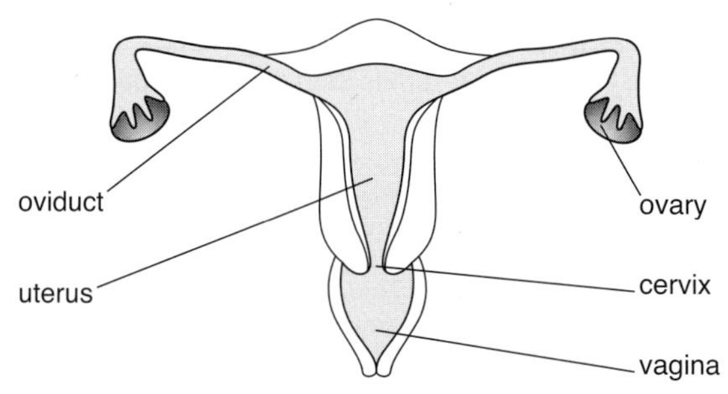
oviduct
ovary
uterus
cervix
vagina

a Use the labels in the diagrams to identify the structures described below. *[5]*

Which structure:

- produces sperm
- adds fluid to sperm
- passes sperm out of the male's body
- releases eggs
- is the place where fertilisation takes place?

b The diagram shows what happens after fertilisation.

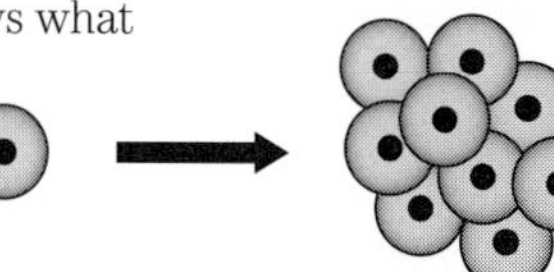

Describe what is happening in the diagram. *[1]*

A few days after this, implantation occurs in the uterus and a foetus grows and develops over the next nine months.

c The diagram (above, right) shows a foetus in the uterus before it is born.

i Which structure, shown in the diagram, cushions the foetus in the uterus against knocks and bumps? *[1]*

ii Which structure, shown in the diagram, allows the foetus to get oxygen from its mother? *[1]*

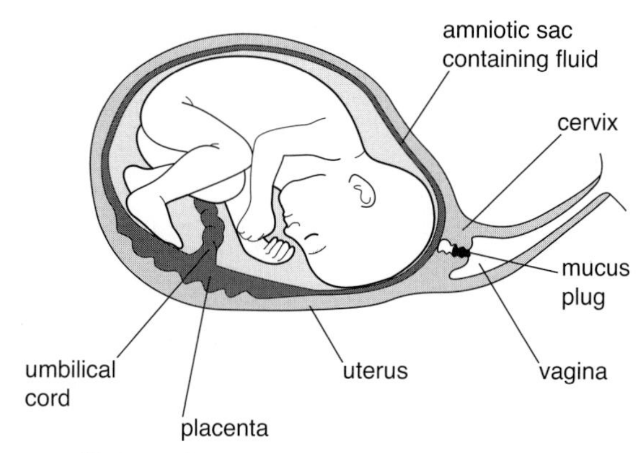
amniotic sac
containing fluid
cervix
mucus
plug
umbilical
cord
uterus
vagina
placenta

iii Copy the passage below which describes the process of birth using the labels in the diagram to fill in the blanks. *[3]*

One of the first signs of labour is when the muscle wall of the ______________ starts to contract. The ______________ widens so that the baby can pass into the ______________. Soon after this, the baby will be born.

d In order to prevent pregnancy different methods of contraception can be used.

i The table shows some information about four different methods of contraception. Copy and complete the table to show how condoms and female sterilisation prevent pregnancy. *[2]*

Method of contraception	How method prevents pregnancy
contraceptive pill	prevents eggs being released
condom	
male sterilisation	prevents sperm from reaching egg
female sterilisation	

ii Which **one** method of contraception, given in the table, can help prevent the spread of sexually transmitted diseases such as AIDS? *[1]*

iii Name **one** method of contraception, given in the table, which is **permanent**. *[1]*

iv Name one **other** sexually transmitted disease. *[1]*

Double Award (Modular)
Paper 1 Foundation
June 2005

2 a The diagram shows the arrangement of blood vessels to the placenta and the foetus.

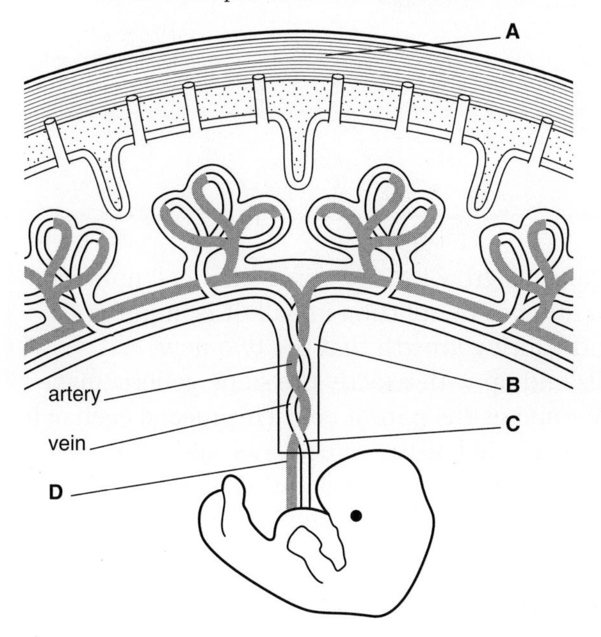
A
artery
B
vein
C
D

i Name **A** and **B**. *[2]*

ii Does the blood flow from the foetus to the placenta or in the opposite direction in structures **C** and **D**? *[1]*

iii Describe and explain how the structure of the foetal blood vessels is adapted for their function in the placenta. *[3]*

b Childless couples can undergo *in-vitro* fertilisation.

i Give **one** cause of infertility in each of males and females. *[2]*

The first stage of *in-vitro* fertilisation involves giving the woman a course of reproductive hormones.

ii Explain the effect of the hormones on the ovary and the uterus. *[2]*

iii Explain why more than one embryo must be placed in the uterus. *[2]*

Biology Paper 2 Higher
June 2006

14

Cell division

Most living organisms grow by increasing their cell number. Cells double in number by splitting in half. It is important when cells divide during growth that the two new (daughter) cells end up with exactly the same genetic make-up as each other and as the parent cell. This means each cell in the growing organism has the same genes and chromosomes. This type of cell division is called **mitosis** and the stages in the process are shown in Figure 14.1.

Figure 14.1 Mitosis (only two pairs of chromosomes are shown)

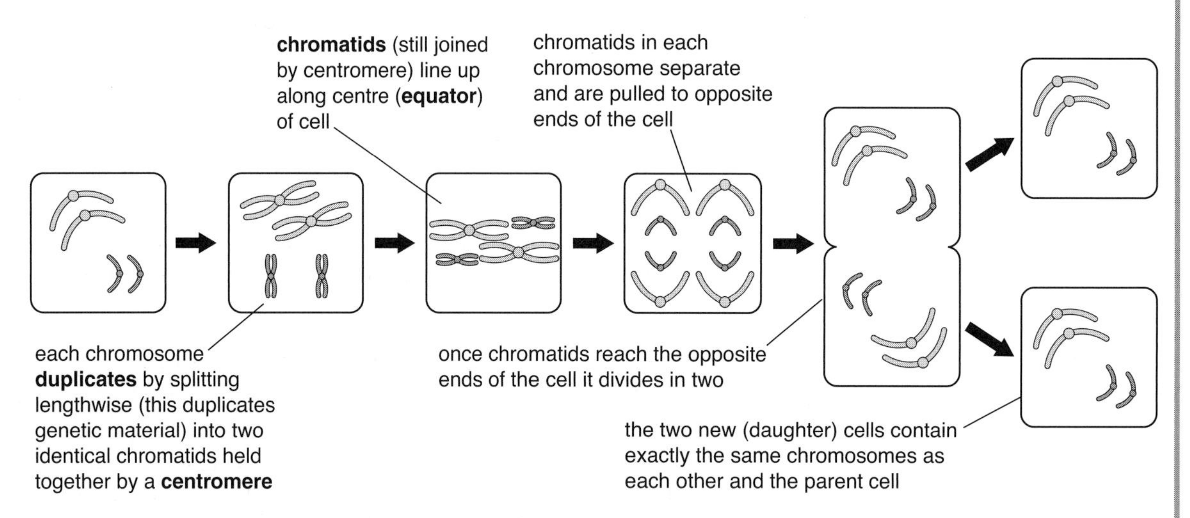

chromatids (still joined by centromere) line up along centre (**equator**) of cell
chromatids in each chromosome separate and are pulled to opposite ends of the cell
each chromosome **duplicates** by splitting lengthwise (this duplicates genetic material) into two identical chromatids held together by a **centromere**
once chromatids reach the opposite ends of the cell it divides in two
the two new (daughter) cells contain exactly the same chromosomes as each other and the parent cell

Meiosis is a different type of cell division and this only takes place in **sex organs** (testes and ovaries) during the production of **gametes** (sperm or eggs). The purpose of meiosis is to produce gametes with half the number of chromosomes of all the other (non-gamete) cells in the body. The stages in the process of meiosis are shown in Figure 14.2.

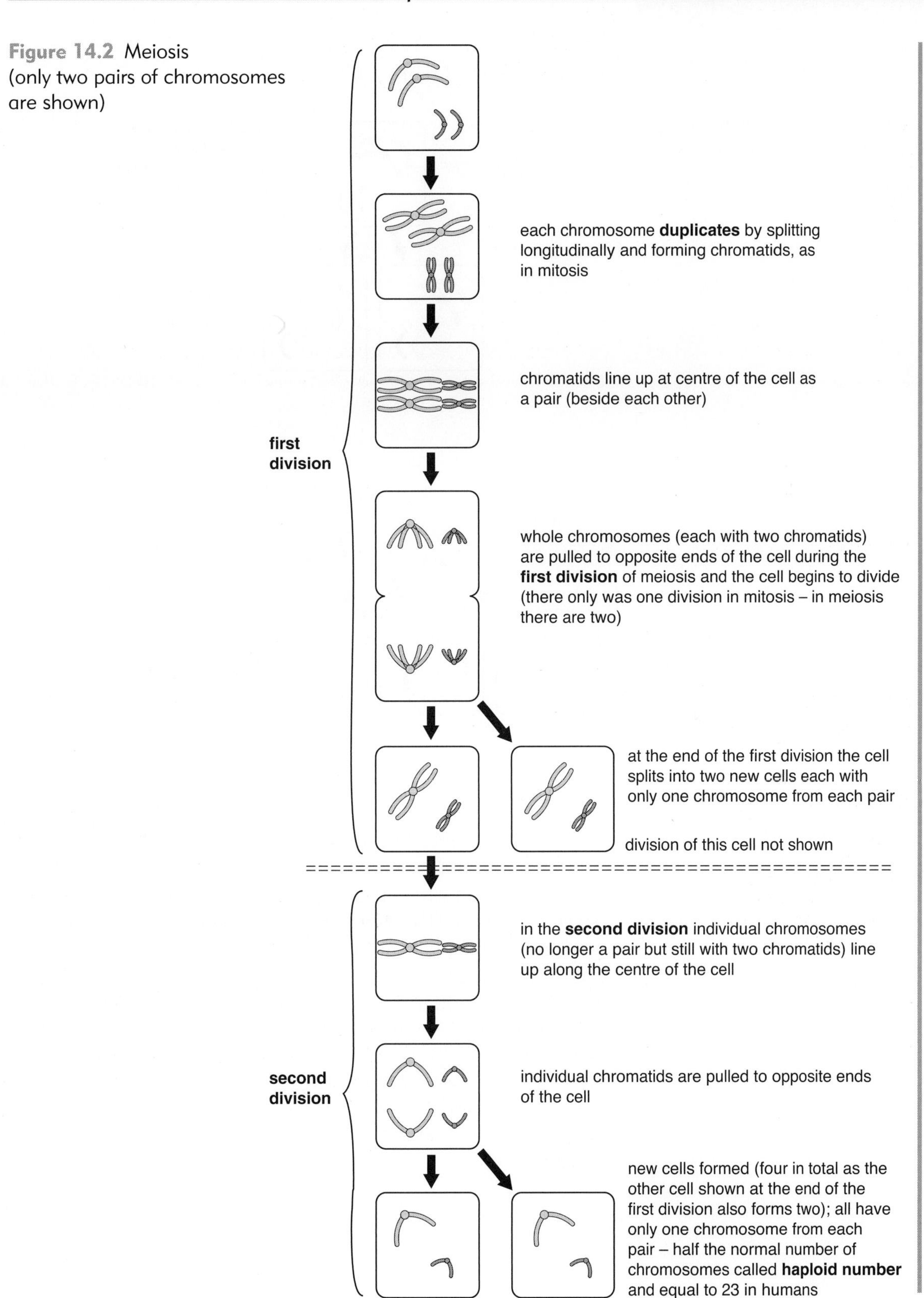
first division
each chromosome **duplicates** by splitting longitudinally and forming chromatids, as in mitosis
chromatids line up at centre of the cell as a pair (beside each other)
whole chromosomes (each with two chromatids) are pulled to opposite ends of the cell during the **first division** of meiosis and the cell begins to divide (there only was one division in mitosis – in meiosis there are two)
at the end of the first division the cell splits into two new cells each with only one chromosome from each pair
division of this cell not shown
second division
in the **second division** individual chromosomes (no longer a pair but still with two chromatids) line up along the centre of the cell
individual chromatids are pulled to opposite ends of the cell
new cells formed (four in total as the other cell shown at the end of the first division also forms two); all have only one chromosome from each pair – half the normal number of chromosomes called **haploid number** and equal to 23 in humans

Figure 14.2 Meiosis (only two pairs of chromosomes are shown)

The differences between the two types of cell division are summarised in Figure 14.3.

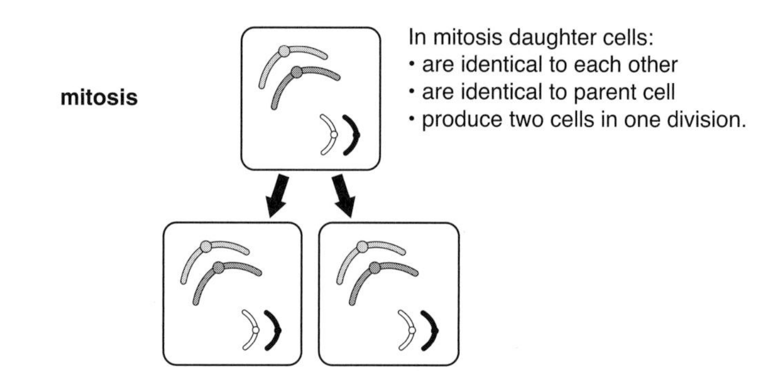
mitosis
In mitosis daughter cells:
• are identical to each other
• are identical to parent cell
• produce two cells in one division.

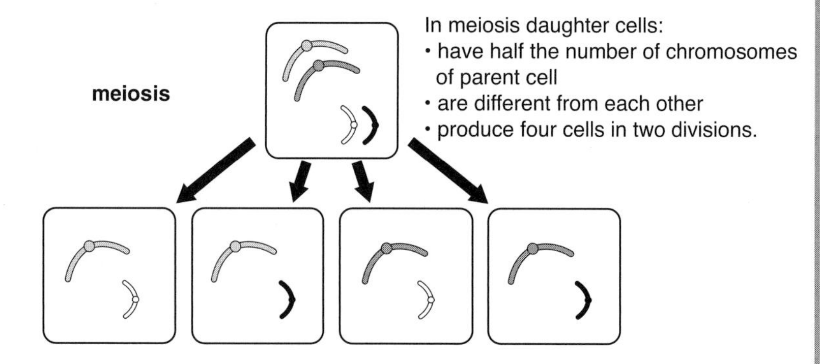
meiosis
In meiosis daughter cells:
• have half the number of chromosomes of parent cell
• are different from each other
• produce four cells in two divisions.

Figure 14.3 The differences between mitosis and meiosis (only two pairs of chromosomes are shown)

What happens to the chromosomes at fertilisation?

When two gametes combine in fertilisation they produce the first cell of a new individual. In humans each gamete has 23 chromosomes (one from each pair of chromosomes) so this first cell (the **zygote**) has 46 (with each pair being restored) as shown in Figure 14.4. Following fertilisation mitosis takes place to ensure that the millions of cells in the adult have identical cells to the zygote (except for the sex cells).

Figure 14.4 Chromosome numbers at fertilisation

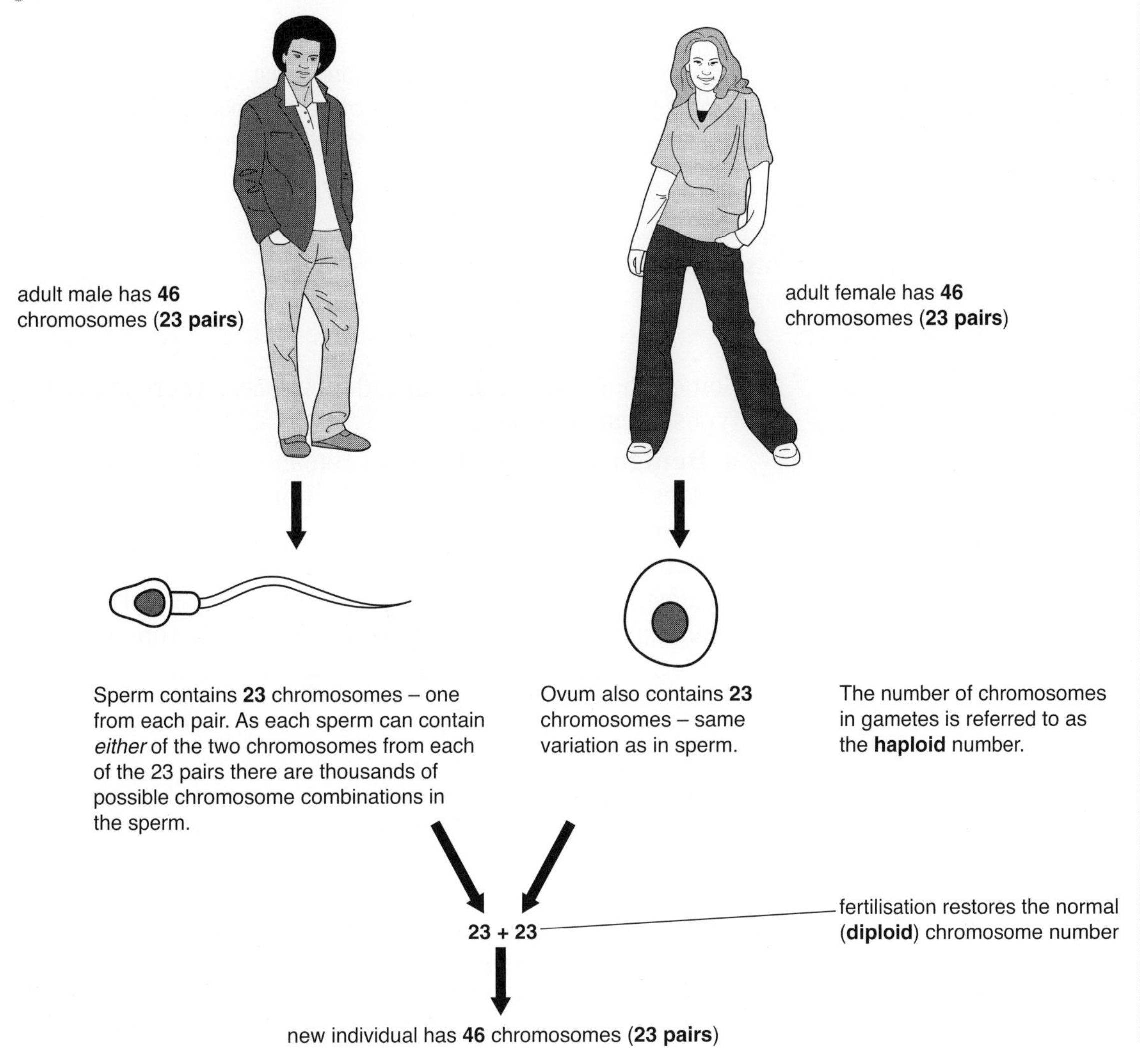
adult male has **46** chromosomes (**23 pairs**)
adult female has **46** chromosomes (**23 pairs**)
Sperm contains **23** chromosomes – one from each pair. As each sperm can contain *either* of the two chromosomes from each of the 23 pairs there are thousands of possible chromosome combinations in the sperm.
Ovum also contains **23** chromosomes – same variation as in sperm.
The number of chromosomes in gametes is referred to as the **haploid** number.
23 + 23
fertilisation restores the normal (**diploid**) chromosome number
new individual has **46** chromosomes (**23 pairs**)

Cancer

Cancer is a term that describes a range of diseases that occur when there is **uncontrolled** or **abnormal cell division**. As well as cell division proceeding unchecked to form a growth or tumour, the cancer cells themselves may appear different, for example they may have very large nuclei. The cancer causes harm by blocking passages in the body and disrupting the work of other cells.

Causes of cancer

Environmental factors such as the tar produced when **smoking** (lung cancer) and **UV light** (skin cancer) can act as triggers to start cancer.

Question

1 a What causes skin cancer? [1]
b Suggest why the number of people with skin cancer in Northern Ireland is rising rapidly. [1]
c Name **three** precautions you should take to reduce the chance of getting skin cancer. [3]

Typical answer

1 a UV radiation/sunlight. [1]
b More people going on foreign holidays/climate change. [1]
c Three of the following points for 3 marks: [3]

- stay out of Sun at hottest times
- wear more clothes/hat
- do not stay in Sun for too long at one time
- use sunscreen.

Some other cancers are caused by viruses. There are two types of cancer tumour.

- **Benign:** this type of tumour remains in one place and does not spread throughout the body; it has a distinct boundary/capsule around it.
- **Malignant:** this type of tumour is not as confined (no capsule) and tends to break off from the original tumour and spread throughout the body. Malignant tumours are more harmful and may affect many more parts of the body.

Treating cancer

If cancer can be detected before a tumour grows too large, and before cancer cells spread around the body from malignant tumours, the chance of successful treatment is much higher. **Screening programmes** such as those for breast, cervical and prostate cancer are in place to provide early detection. Once cancer has been diagnosed some of the treatment options are shown in Figure 14.5.

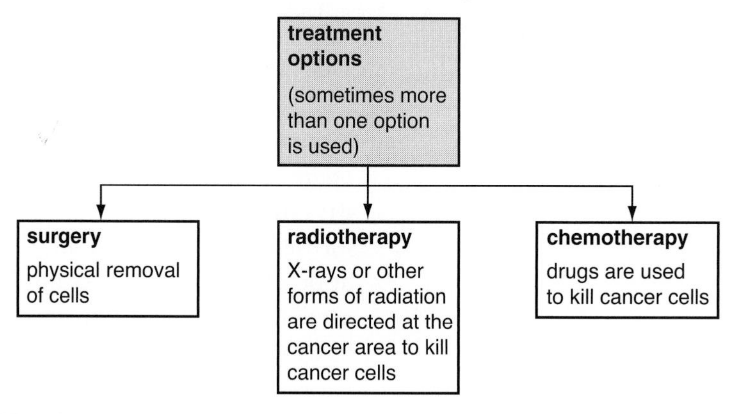
treatment options
(sometimes more than one option is used)
surgery
physical removal of cells
radiotherapy
X-rays or other forms of radiation are directed at the cancer area to kill cancer cells
chemotherapy
drugs are used to kill cancer cells

Figure 14.5 Some of the treatments for cancer

The decision of which treatment to use depends on the type of cancer and each method has disadvantages. The treatments can damage normal cells in the body as well as cancer cells and the side-effects of chemotherapy can be very severe.

Exam questions

1 The diagram shows part of the human life cycle.

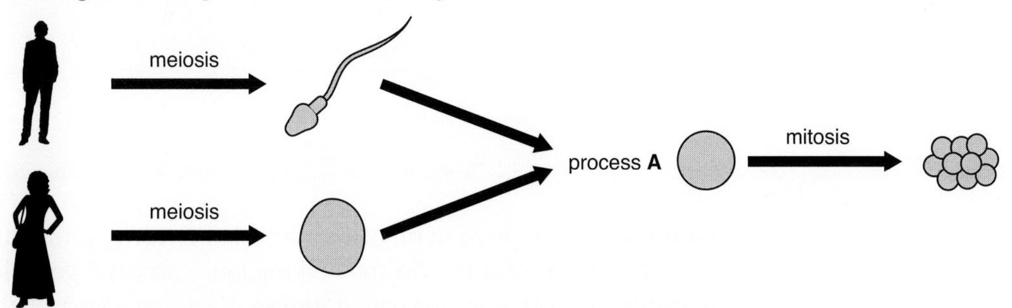
meiosis
meiosis
process **A**
mitosis

a Copy the diagram and draw and label on it a haploid nucleus and a diploid nucleus. *[2]*
b Name Process **A**. *[1]*
c Give a place in the body where meiosis occurs. *[1]*
d Give **two** differences between mitosis and meiosis. *[2]*

Biology Paper 1 Higher June 2003

2 **a** The diagrams show a cross-section through the bladder of a healthy man and one with prostate cancer.

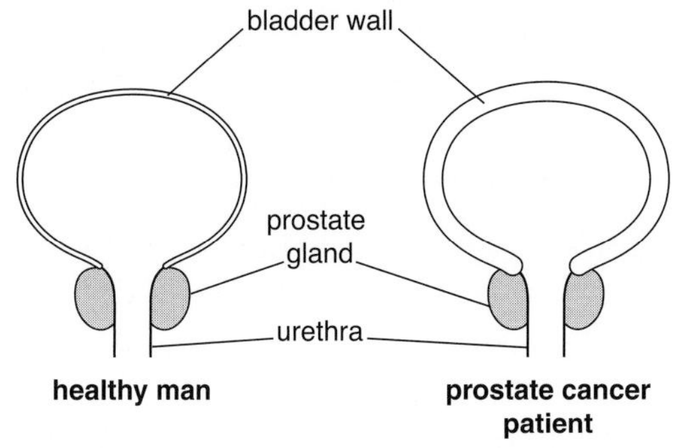
bladder wall
prostate gland
urethra
healthy man
prostate cancer patient

i Give **one** way the cancer patient's bladder differs from that of a healthy man. *[1]*
ii What is cancer? *[2]*

b Men can be screened for prostate cancer.
i What is screening? *[1]*
ii Give **one** advantage of a screening programme. *[1]*

Biology Paper 1 Foundation June 2006

15

Genetics

Genetics is the passing on of characteristics from parents to offspring. Chromosomes in the cell nucleus carry the genetic material in short sections called **genes**. Each gene carries the code for a particular characteristic, for example eye colour. As chromosomes occur in pairs each chromosome in a pair carries the same gene (for example for eye colour) but the gene for eye colour may have different forms (called **alleles**) in the two chromosomes (one allele may be for brown eyes and one for blue eyes). This is shown in Figure 15.1.

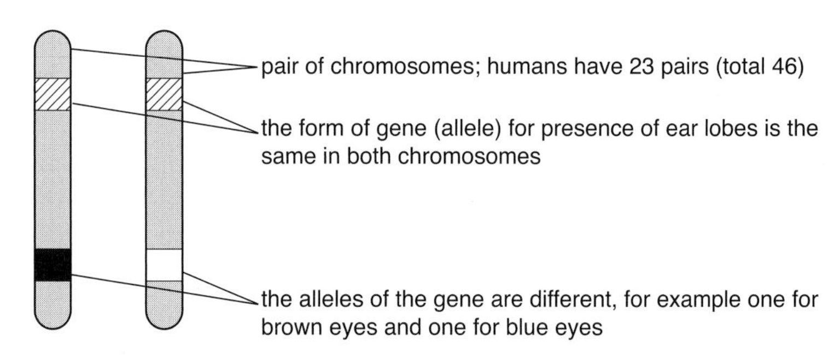
pair of chromosomes; humans have 23 pairs (total 46)
the form of gene (allele) for presence of ear lobes is the same in both chromosomes
the alleles of the gene are different, for example one for brown eyes and one for blue eyes

Figure 15.1 Arrangement of alleles in a chromosome pair

Some of the key genetic terms are defined in Table 15.1.

Table 15.1 Definitions of some important genetic terms

Term	Definition	Example
gene	short section of chromosome that codes for a particular characteristic	gene for eye colour
allele	a particular form of a gene	brown eyes and blue eyes are different alleles of the eye colour gene
homozygous	both alleles of a gene are the same	both alleles are for brown eyes
heterozygous	alleles of a gene are different	one allele is for brown eyes and the other is for blue eyes (Figure 15.1)

Note: Genetics questions normally involve asking you to work out what the offspring are from particular parents (sometimes you are asked to work backwards and work out the parents). Figure 15.2 shows how to set out the cross when you are asked to work out the offspring produced from two **heterozygous** parents using the example of height in peas. Peas can be either tall or dwarf and this is controlled by a single gene that has tall and dwarf alleles. A cross involving one characteristic (for example height) is a **monohybrid** cross.

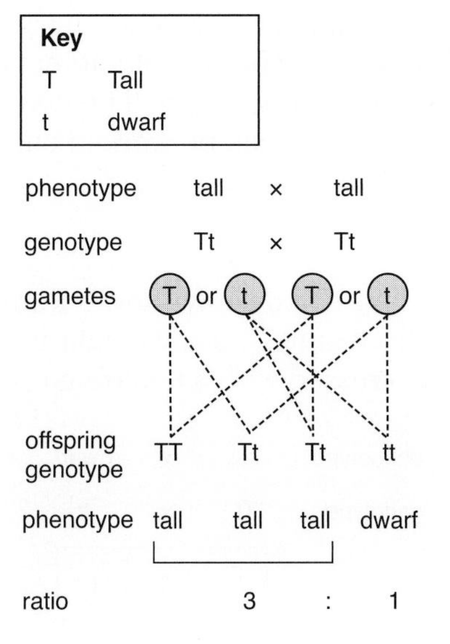
Key
T Tall
t dwarf
phenotype tall × tall
genotype Tt × Tt
gametes T or t T or t
offspring genotype TT Tt Tt tt
phenotype tall tall tall dwarf
ratio 3 : 1
Either (but not both) of the two genotype alleles can pass into a gamete; in this example each parent produces equal numbers of T and t gametes.
There is an equal chance of either gamete from a parent combining with either gamete of the other parent; this produces the offspring in the ratio 3:1.

Figure 15.2 How to set out a cross when answering a genetics question

Some other important terms that are in Figure 15.2 are defined in Table 15.2.

Table 15.2 More definitions of genetic terms

Term	Definition	Example
genotype	paired symbols showing the allele arrangement in an individual	parents in Figure 15.2 have the genotype Tt
phenotype	outward appearance of an individual	parents in Figure 15.2 have a tall phenotype
dominant	in the heterozygous condition the dominant allele overrides the non-dominant (recessive) allele	parents in Figure 15.2 are both tall even through they are heterozygous and have a dwarf allele
recessive	recessive allele is dominated by the dominant allele – it only shows itself in the phenotype if there are two recessive alleles	only one-quarter of the offspring in the cross are dwarf as only one-quarter have no dominant T allele present

Note: Some other important points about genetic crosses are listed below and overleaf.

- It is very important to get the gametes correct. This is probably where most mistakes are made at GCSE level. Remember there is only one symbol in each gamete (only one chromosome and therefore one allele from a pair of chromosomes enters a gamete). If the parents are heterozygous then there are two possible types of gametes and if they are homozygous there is only one type of gamete.
- Ratios are only accurate when large numbers of offspring are involved. For example the 3:1 ratio in the earlier example may only be accurate if there are large numbers. This is because the mixing of gametes (and alleles) is entirely random during fertilisation.

- Sometimes the offspring are referred to as the **F1 generation** and if parents are described as **pure breeding** they will be homozygous.
- Crosses can be worked out using **Punnett squares**.

The Punnett square

Figure 15.3 shows how a Punnett square can be used. In this example, using height in peas as before, a heterozygote is crossed with a homozygous recessive pea.

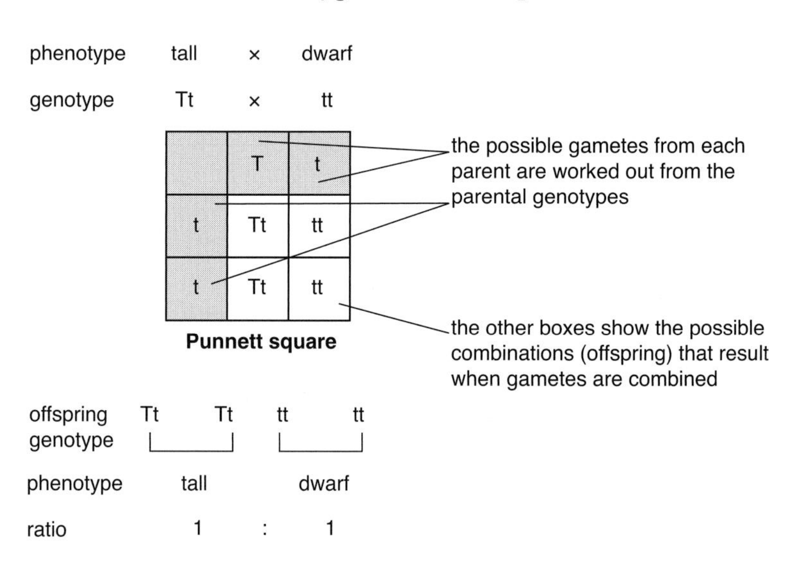
phenotype tall × dwarf
genotype Tt × tt
T
t
t
Tt
tt
t
Tt
tt
the possible gametes from each parent are worked out from the parental genotypes
Punnett square
the other boxes show the possible combinations (offspring) that result when gametes are combined
offspring genotype Tt Tt tt tt
phenotype tall dwarf
ratio 1 : 1

Figure 15.3 How to use a Punnett square

Question

1 Brown eyes are dominant to blue eyes. Using the symbols B = brown and b = blue show how brown-eyed parents can have children with blue eyes. *[4]*

Typical answer

1 *[4]*

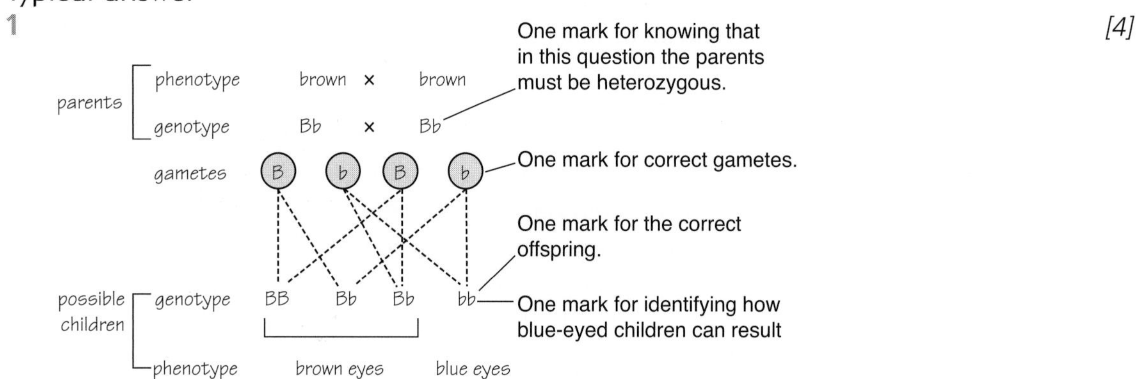
parents
phenotype brown × brown
genotype Bb × Bb
gametes B b B b
possible children
genotype BB Bb Bb bb
phenotype brown eyes blue eyes
One mark for knowing that in this question the parents must be heterozygous.
One mark for correct gametes.
One mark for the correct offspring.
One mark for identifying how blue-eyed children can result

The test cross (back cross)

Individuals that are homozygous dominant or heterozygous have different genotypes but the same phenotype. The **test cross** can be used to determine the genotype of an individual of dominant phenotype but unknown genotype as shown in Figure 15.4.

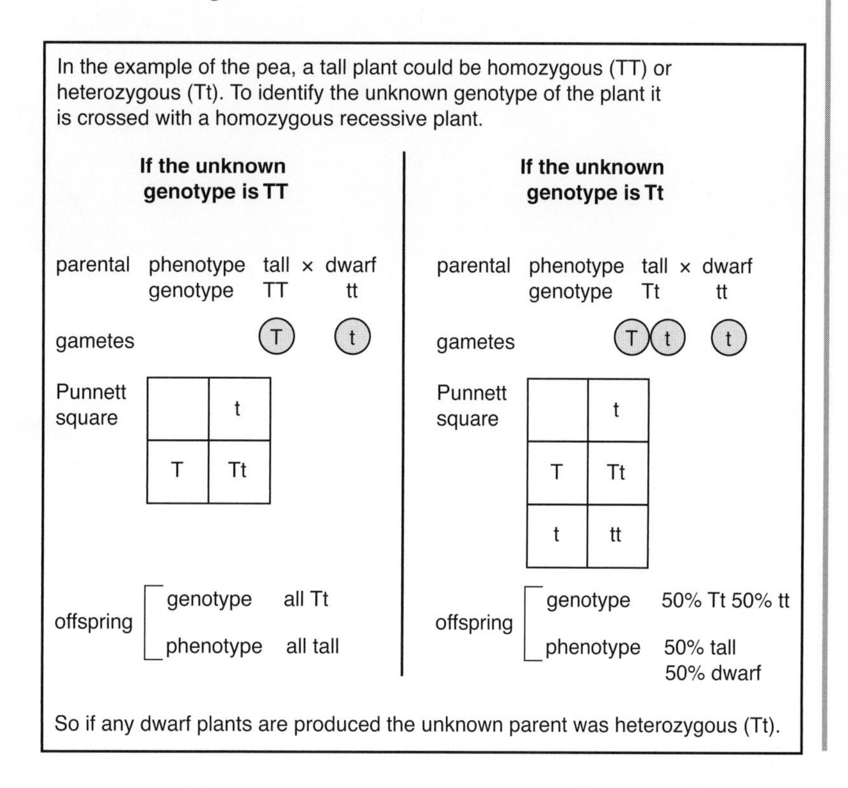
In the example of the pea, a tall plant could be homozygous (TT) or heterozygous (Tt). To identify the unknown genotype of the plant it is crossed with a homozygous recessive plant.
If the unknown genotype is TT
parental phenotype tall × dwarf
genotype TT tt
gametes T t
Punnett square
t
T Tt
offspring
genotype all Tt
phenotype all tall
If the unknown genotype is Tt
parental phenotype tall × dwarf
genotype Tt tt
gametes T t t
Punnett square
t
T Tt
t tt
offspring
genotype 50% Tt 50% tt
phenotype 50% tall 50% dwarf
So if any dwarf plants are produced the unknown parent was heterozygous (Tt).

Figure 15.4 The test cross

Sex determination in humans

Humans have 22 pairs of normal chromosomes and one pair of sex chromosomes. The male sex chromosomes are XY and females have two XX chromosomes. As the sex chromosomes (and alleles) act in the same way as in other genetic crosses, Figure 15.5 on the next page shows that equal numbers of boys and girls are produced.

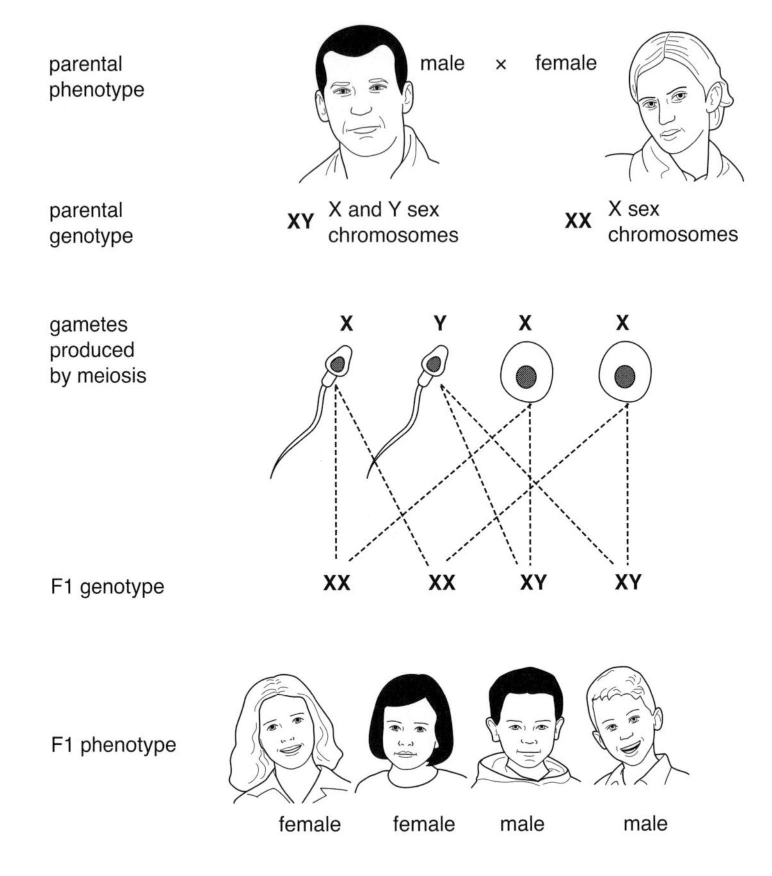
parental phenotype
male × female
parental genotype
XY X and Y sex chromosomes
XX X sex chromosomes
gametes produced by meiosis
X
Y
X
X
F1 genotype
XX
XX
XY
XY
F1 phenotype
female
female
male
male

Figure 15.5 How equal numbers of boys and girls are produced

Inherited diseases

Genetics can explain how some diseases are inherited and can run in families (cystic fibrosis) or can arise due to genetic malfunction (Down's syndrome).

Cystic fibrosis

Cystic fibrosis is caused by a recessive allele. Individuals with cystic fibrosis must have both alleles – cc.
If two parents are **carriers** (are heterozygous, Cc, containing the allele but have a normal phenotype) there is a 25% probability that a child will be homozygous and have cystic fibrosis.

Down's syndrome

This condition is not caused by a recessive allele but by an error in the formation of the parental gametes.
In this condition a malformed gamete of 24 chromosomes combines with a normal gamete of 23 chromosomes. The affected individual has 47 chromosomes in all their cells which causes the condition Down's syndrome.

Sex linkage

As well as determining sex, sex chromosomes can carry genes and alleles that control other characteristics. As the Y chromosome does not contain any alleles, any recessive alleles carried on the X chromosome are not masked by a dominant partner and therefore will show in the phenotype. In females where there are two X chromosomes the recessive condition can be masked by a dominant allele. Examples of sex-linked conditions are red-green colour blindness and haemophilia as shown in Figure 15.6.

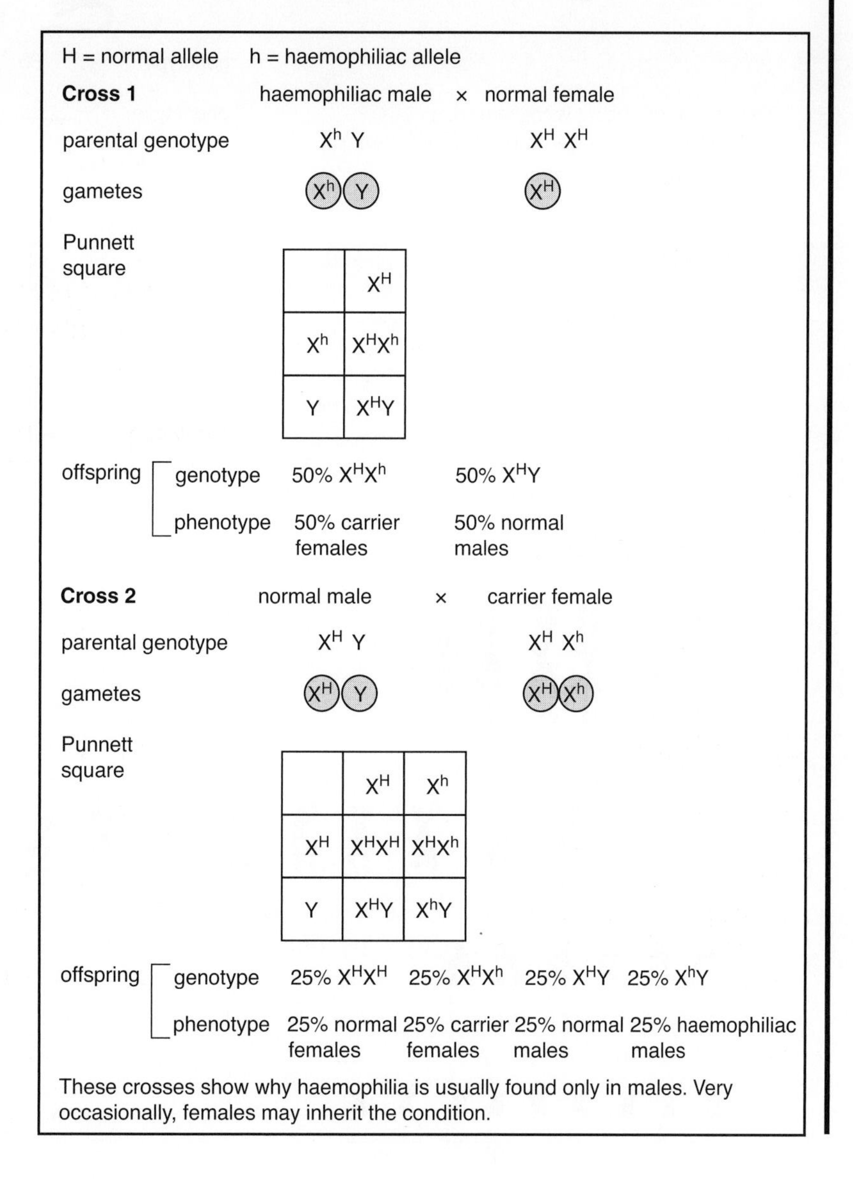
H = normal allele h = haemophiliac allele
Cross 1
haemophiliac male × normal female
parental genotype
X^h Y
X^H X^H
gametes
X^h Y
X^H
Punnett square
X^H
X^h X^HX^h
Y X^HY
offspring
genotype 50% X^HX^h 50% X^HY
phenotype 50% carrier females 50% normal males
Cross 2
normal male × carrier female
parental genotype
X^H Y
X^H X^h
gametes
X^H Y
X^H X^h
Punnett square
X^H X^h
X^H X^HX^H X^HX^h
Y X^HY X^hY
offspring
genotype 25% X^HX^H 25% X^HX^h 25% X^HY 25% X^hY
phenotype 25% normal females 25% carrier females 25% normal males 25% haemophiliac males
These crosses show why haemophilia is usually found only in males. Very occasionally, females may inherit the condition.

Figure 15.6 The sex-linked condition called haemophilia

Exam questions

1 The diagram (on the right) shows a genetic cross between two pure bred mice. Black coat (B) is dominant to white coat (b).

a Give the genotype of the white parent and the phenotype of the offspring. *[2]*

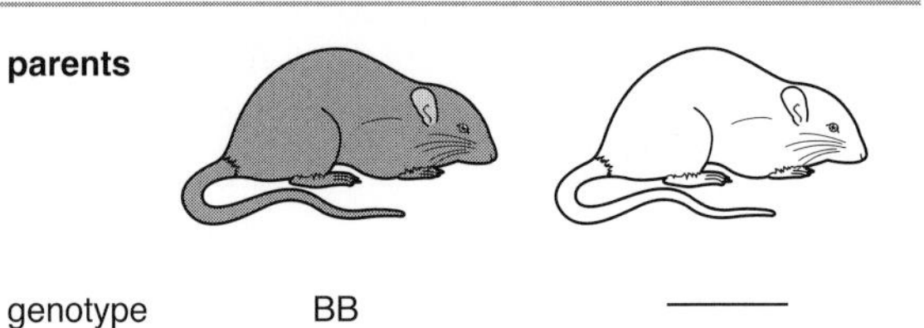
parents
genotype BB ______

offspring

genotype Bb

phenotype ______

Two of the offspring were mated.

b **i** Copy and complete the Punnett square (right) to show this cross. *[3]*

ii Draw a circle round the homozygous recessive offspring. *[1]*

iii Give the expected ratio of black mice to white mice. *[1]*

iv Explain what is meant by recessive. *[1]*

v Explain the terms heterozygous and homozygous. *[2]*

parents: Bb × Bb

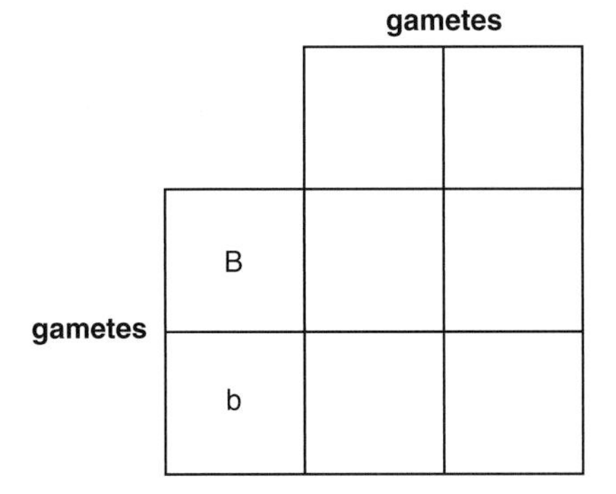
gametes
gametes
B
b

c The alleles for black and white coats are two forms of a gene.

i What is a gene? *[1]*

ii Where are genes found in the cell? *[2]*

d The diagram shows a set of chromosomes from a human cell.

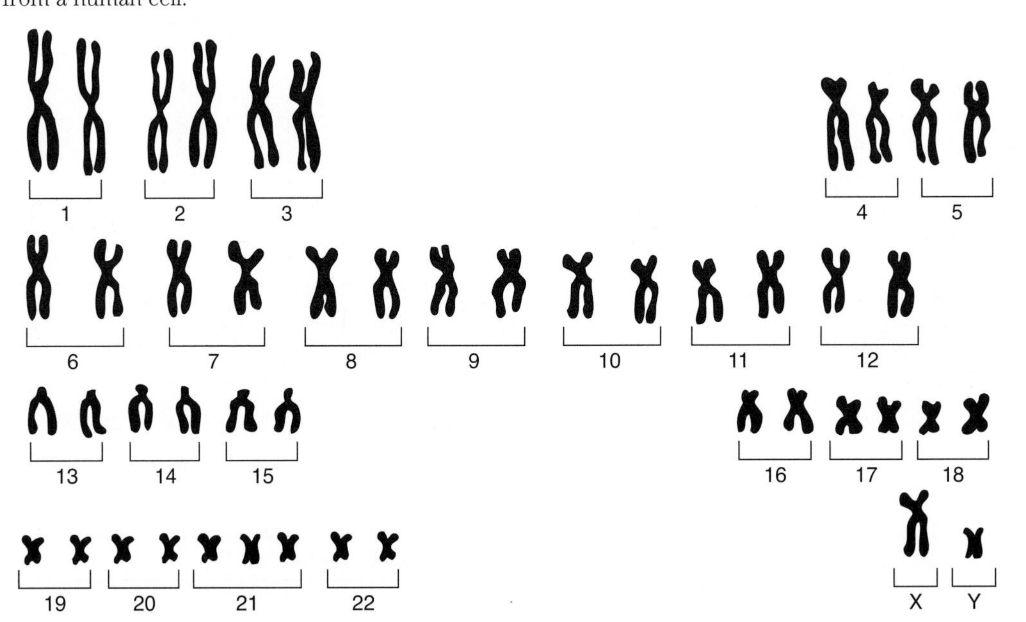
1
2
3
4
5
6
7
8
9
10
11
12
13
14
15
16
17
18
19
20
21
22
X
Y

Use the information in the diagram to help answer the following questions.

i Give the sex of the person the cell was taken from and give a reason for your answer. *[2]*
The chromosomes show an abnormality.
ii Describe how these chromosomes differ from normal chromosomes and suggest the genetic condition the person would be affected by. *[2]*
iii What term describes a change in a chromosome? *[1]*

Biology Paper 2 Foundation June 2006

2 a The plumage of Rock Doves usually shows two distinct wing bars. Occasionally Rock Doves with no wing bars will occur in the population.

bars on
wings

The gene (allele) for wing bars is dominant to the gene (allele) for no wing bars.
Let B = gene (allele) for wing bars
Let b = gene (allele) for no wing bars

i Use a Punnett square to show how Rock Doves with no wing bars may be produced from parents with wing bars. *[4]*
ii Explain why it is not possible to tell the genotype of a Rock Dove which is homozygous dominant for wing bars from a Rock Dove which is heterozygous. *[1]*
iii Explain how a backcross could be used to determine the genotype of the doves in part **ii**. *[4]*

Double Award (Non-modular) Paper 1 Higher June 2004

3 The diagram shows the inheritance of colour-blindness, a sex-linked disease, in one family.
i In the diagram what relationship is 5 to 2? *[1]*
ii Explain sex-linkage. *[2]*
iii Explain why colour-blind males are more common than colour-blind females. *[2]*
iv Suggest why the sons of parents 5 and 6 are not colour-blind. *[2]*
v Select **one** marriage which could produce a daughter suffering from colour-blindness and describe all the offspring from this cross.
Let X^N represent the allele for normal sight
and X^n the allele for colour-blindness. *[4]*

Biology Paper 2 Higher June 2003

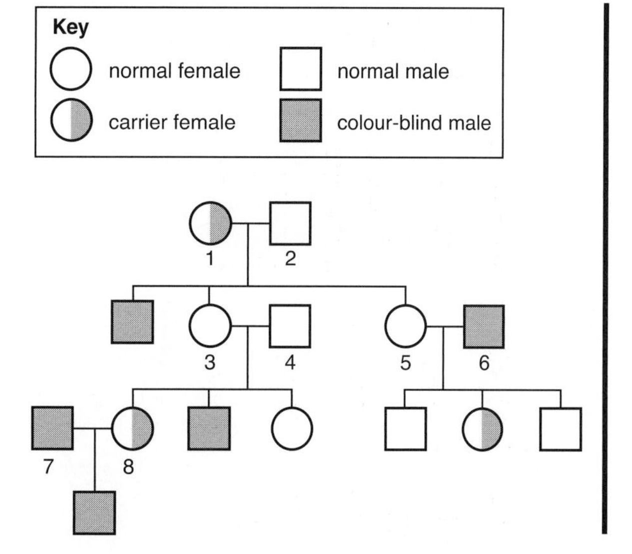
Key
normal female
normal male
carrier female
colour-blind male
1
2
3
4
5
6
7
8

16

DNA – the hereditary material

The structure of DNA

Figure 16.1 shows the structure of DNA (deoxyribose nucleic acid).

Figure 16.1 The structure of DNA

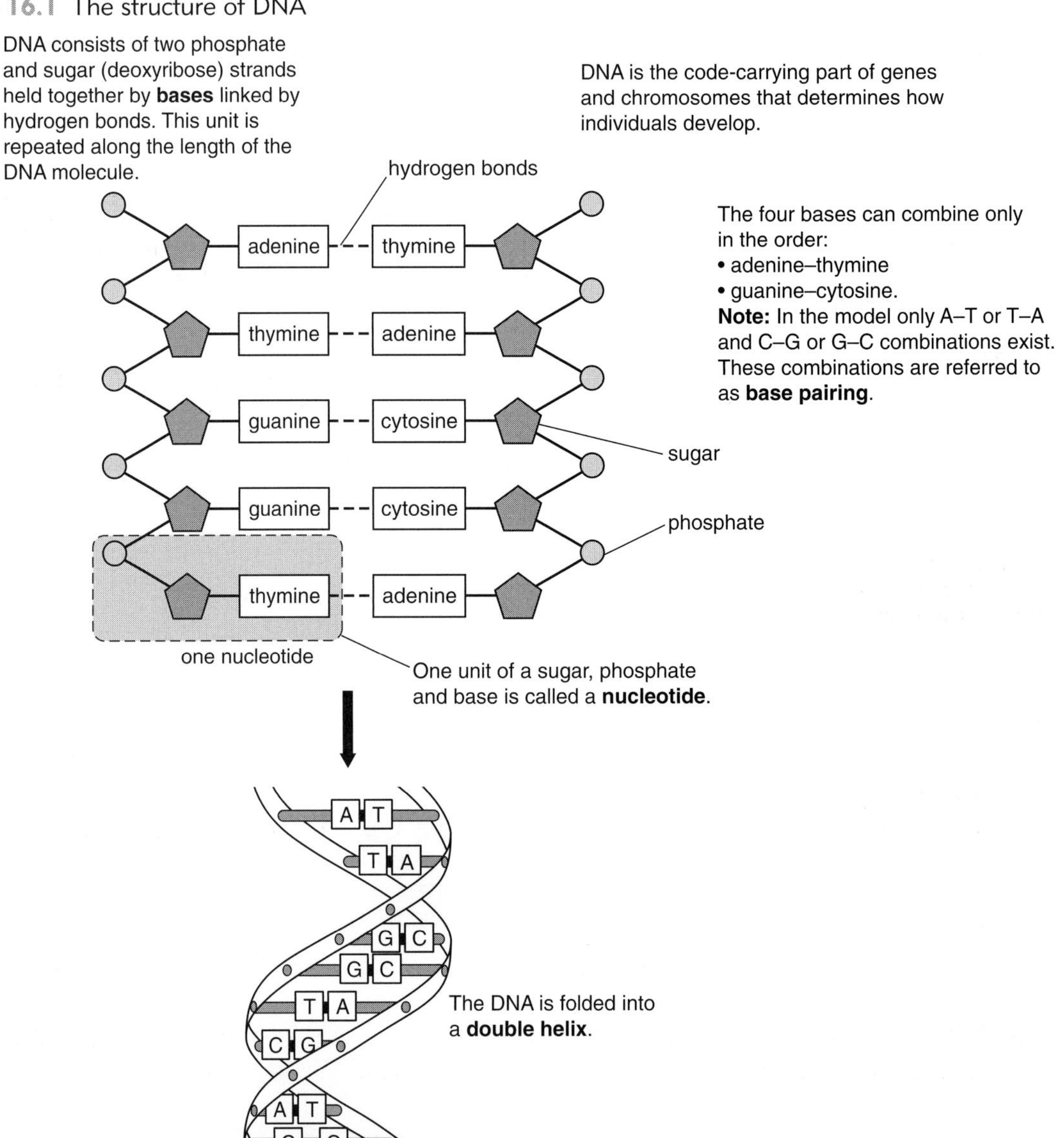

DNA consists of two phosphate and sugar (deoxyribose) strands held together by **bases** linked by hydrogen bonds. This unit is repeated along the length of the DNA molecule.
DNA is the code-carrying part of genes and chromosomes that determines how individuals develop.
hydrogen bonds
adenine
thymine
thymine
adenine
guanine
cytosine
guanine
cytosine
thymine
adenine
The four bases can combine only in the order:
• adenine–thymine
• guanine–cytosine.
Note: In the model only A–T or T–A and C–G or G–C combinations exist. These combinations are referred to as **base pairing**.
sugar
phosphate
one nucleotide
One unit of a sugar, phosphate and base is called a **nucleotide**.
A T
T A
G C
G C
T A
C G
A T
C G
G C
The DNA is folded into a **double helix**.

How does DNA work?

Deoxyribose nucleic acid works by coding for different amino acids which then combine to form proteins, as shown in Figure 16.2.

Figure 16.2 How DNA works

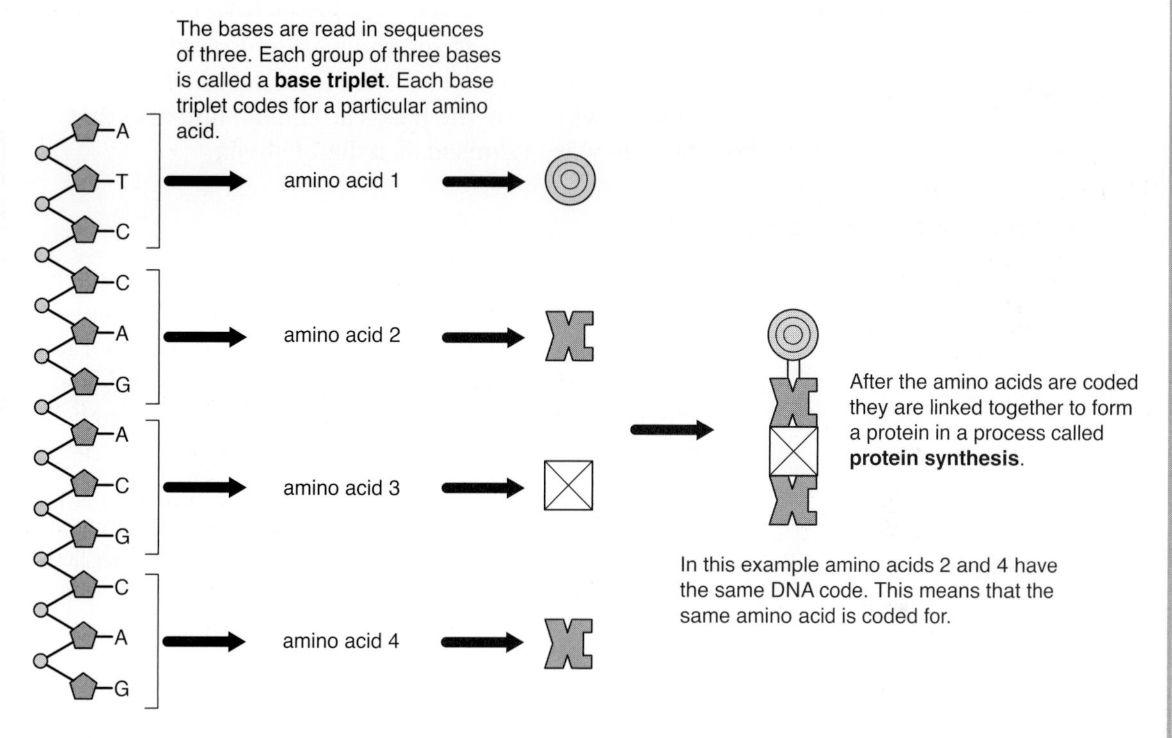
The bases are read in sequences of three. Each group of three bases is called a **base triplet**. Each base triplet codes for a particular amino acid.
A
T
C
C
A
G
A
C
G
C
A
G
amino acid 1
amino acid 2
amino acid 3
amino acid 4
After the amino acids are coded they are linked together to form a protein in a process called **protein synthesis**.
In this example amino acids 2 and 4 have the same DNA code. This means that the same amino acid is coded for.
Only one strand of the DNA (the coding strand) is involved in the coding process.

Question

1 a A length of DNA consists of 180 bases. How many amino acids does this section code for? Explain your answer. [2]

b In the same section 60 of the bases are thymine. How many guanine bases are there in the section? [2]

Typical answer

1 a *30; only half the bases (90) are in the coding strand; in the coding strand each sequence of three bases (a triplet) produces one amino acid.* [2]

b *If 60 = thymine then 60 = adenine; A and T always code together (total 120); remaining 60 must be 30 guanine and 30 cytosine (C and G always code together).* [2]

Working out the structure of DNA

Franklin and Wilkins

Using X-ray diffraction Franklin and Wilkins worked out the 3D shape of the molecule but were not sure how the molecule fitted together.

Watson and Crick

Using knowledge gained from the work of Franklin and Wilkins, Watson and Crick built a 3D model of DNA including showing how the bases are linked and also that the molecule was organised as a double helix.

Genetic engineering

In genetic engineering a piece of DNA (gene) can be taken from one organism and incorporated into another organism. Typically a gene that makes a useful product is incorporated into bacteria and the bacteria then become a 'factory' that make the desired product. An example is making human insulin for the treatment of people with diabetes and the steps involved are shown in Figure 16.3.

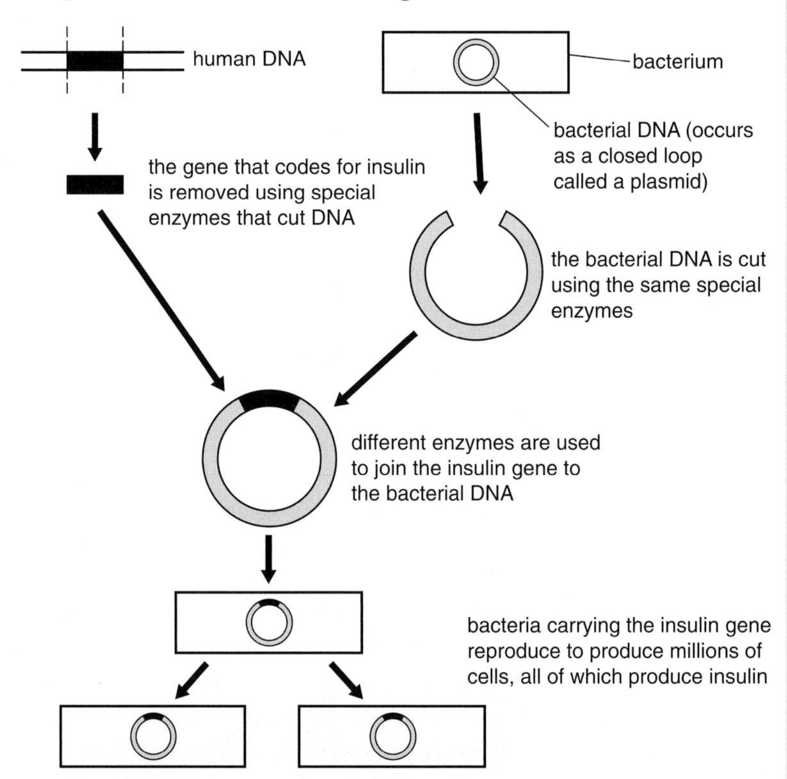
human DNA
bacterium
bacterial DNA (occurs as a closed loop called a plasmid)
the gene that codes for insulin is removed using special enzymes that cut DNA
the bacterial DNA is cut using the same special enzymes
different enzymes are used to join the insulin gene to the bacterial DNA
bacteria carrying the insulin gene reproduce to produce millions of cells, all of which produce insulin
the bacteria are grown in large fermenters that provide the best conditions for bacterial reproduction and allow easy extraction of insulin

Figure 16.3 Genetic engineering – making insulin

Mutations – a change to the DNA code

Genetic engineering involves deliberately changing the code. **Mutations** occur when the code changes naturally and accidentally, although the possibility of them occurring can be increased by environmental factors such as with UV light and skin cancer (see page 93).

Two examples of different types of mutation are listed in Table 16.1.

Table 16.1 Two types of mutation

Type of mutation	Example	Result of mutation
gene	haemophilia	mutant allele will not make Factor 8, a chemical required for the clotting of blood
chromosome number	Down's syndrome	one parent produces a faulty gamete with 24 chromosomes instead of 23 and when this combines with a gamete with 23 chromosomes then the affected individual has 47 (not 46) chromosomes

DNA replication

During mitosis DNA (as well as the chromosomes that contain it) needs to duplicate so that the new cells contain exactly the same DNA as the parent cell. This is called **DNA replication** and involves the molecule splitting and the 'free bases' forming new base pairs with the raw materials to make DNA that is found in the nucleus as shown in Figure 16.4.

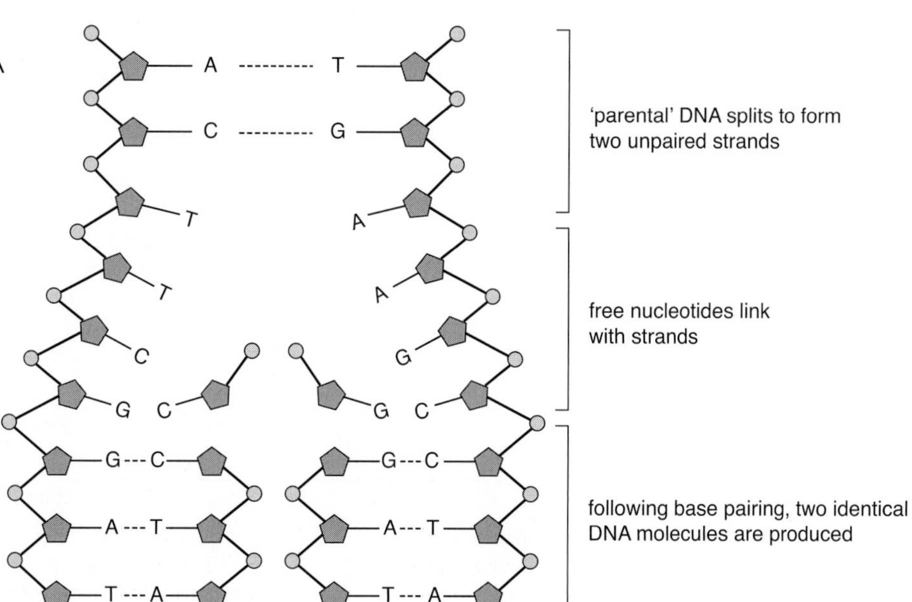
A ---------- T
C ---------- G
T
A
T
A
C
G
G C
G C
G---C
A---T
T---A
G---C
A---T
T---A
'parental' DNA splits to form two unpaired strands
free nucleotides link with strands
following base pairing, two identical DNA molecules are produced

Figure 16.4 The process of DNA replication

Exam questions

1 The diagram shows part of a DNA molecule.

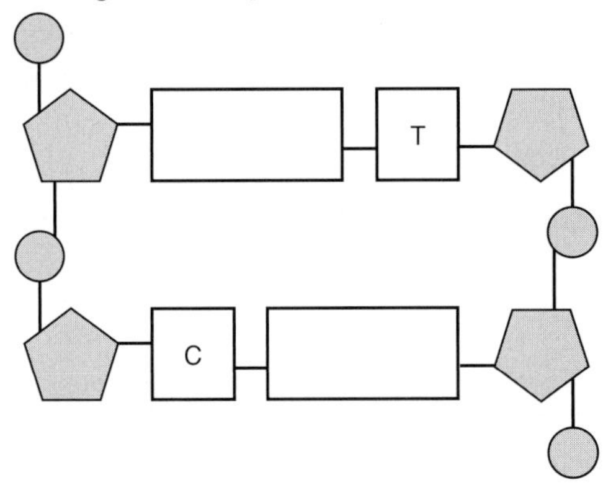
T
C

i Name the two letters missing from the boxes. *[2]*

ii Name the three-dimensional shape of the DNA molecule. *[1]*

One strand of the DNA molecule carries the codes for particular amino acids.

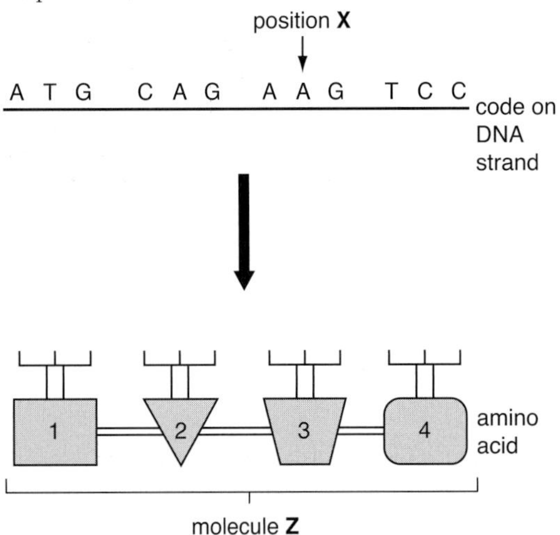
position **X**
A T G C A G A A G T C C
code on DNA strand
1
2
3
4
amino acid
molecule **Z**

Use the diagram to help answer the following questions.

iii Suggest how many bases code for one amino acid. *[1]*

iv Name molecule **Z**. *[1]*

v Give **two** possible uses of molecule **Z** in the body. *[2]*

vi Suggest what would have happened if the base at position **X** changed from **A** to **T**. *[2]*

Biology Paper 2 Higher June 2005

2 a The following diagram (above, right) shows part of a DNA molecule.
Use the information in the diagram and your knowledge to help answer the following questions.

i What term describes the shape of the DNA molecule? *[2]*

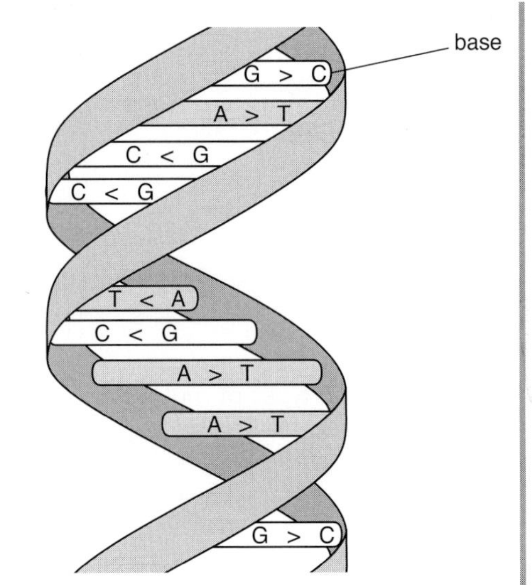
base
G > C
A > T
C < G
C < G
T < A
C < G
A > T
A > T
G > C

ii How many different types of base are there in a DNA molecule? *[1]*

iii Lengths of DNA are called genes. What type of molecule in cells do genes code for? *[1]*

b The diagram shows steps in a genetic engineering process which allows bacteria to make human insulin.

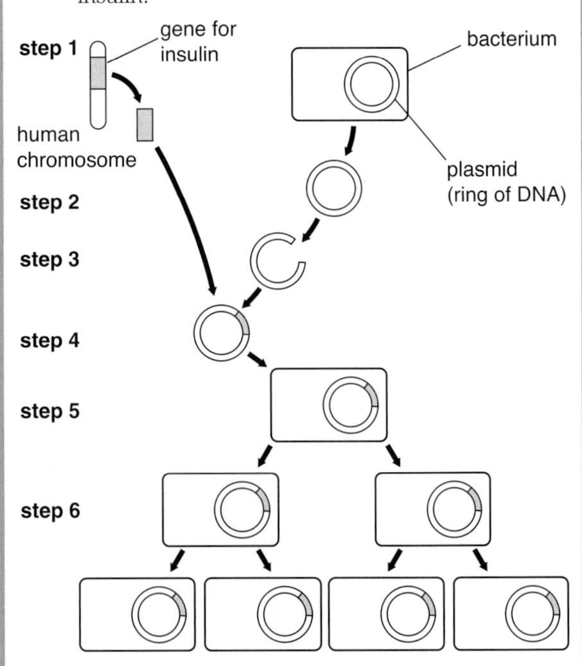
step 1
gene for insulin
bacterium
human chromosome
plasmid (ring of DNA)
step 2
step 3
step 4
step 5
step 6

i Use the diagram and your knowledge to describe what is happening at each step. *[5]*

ii Why do these bacteria produce human insulin? *[1]*

Double Award (Non-modular) Paper 1 Higher June 2006

17 Variation, selection and evolution

Living organisms that belong to the same species resemble each other but they usually differ from each other in a number of ways. These differences are called **variation** and Figure 17.1 gives examples of variation.

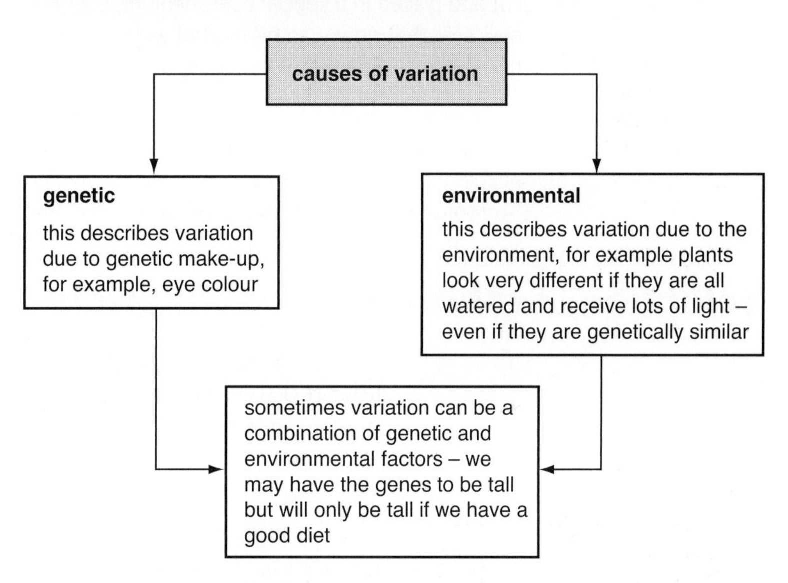
causes of variation
genetic
this describes variation due to genetic make-up, for example, eye colour
environmental
this describes variation due to the environment, for example plants look very different if they are all watered and receive lots of light – even if they are genetically similar
sometimes variation can be a combination of genetic and environmental factors – we may have the genes to be tall but will only be tall if we have a good diet

Figure 17.1 Examples of variation

Variation can be **continuous** or **discontinuous** as shown in Table 17.1.

Table 17.1 Continuous and discontinuous variation

Variation	Explanation	Examples
continuous	gradual change in a characteristic across a population with no distinct categories; most individuals will be average with fewer at either extreme	height; weight; reaction time
discontinuous	individuals can be grouped into distinct groups with no overlap	tongue rolling; blood group

Sexual reproduction produces **variation** due to the random way in which chromosomes combine during fertilisation, whereas **asexual reproduction** produces **clones**.

Cloning – the production of identical offspring

Table 17.2 shows examples of types of cloning.

Table 17.2 Types of cloning

Type of cloning	Method	Advantages
runners	some plants, for example strawberry, produce runners that spread over the ground and produce new genetically identical plants at intervals	only one parent needed; can rapidly colonise an area
cuttings	small parts of the plant stem can be cut and placed in compost; aided by a rooting hormone	many identical plants are produced from the parent
tissue culture	laboratory based; small sections of the plant are cut and placed in a special agar medium; the new cells that grow can be treated with hormones and develop into young plants	produces large numbers relatively quickly; relatively inexpensive; takes place all year round; produces disease-free varieties
embryo cloning	embryos are removed from agricultural animals, for example cattle, and are split into smaller balls of cells which are implanted into other 'surrogate' cows where they develop	large numbers of genetically identical animals can be produced that have desirable commercial characteristics

Selection, evolution and extinction

If the members of a species vary then some will be better adapted to survive than others. For example the faster, healthier prey is more likely to escape the predator than the slow disease-ridden individual. This means that the best adapted or fittest survive which is the basis for **evolution** – small changes over time can mean that organisms change as particular characteristics are favoured.

Sometimes **entire species** may not be well enough adapted to survive in a changing world and they no longer survive. For example mammoths did not survive the last ice age and flightless birds could not survive when man colonised the remote islands they lived on and used them as food – they became **extinct**.

Selection and Charles Darwin

Charles Darwin concluded that **natural selection** was the driving force for evolution. His main points were:

- variation exits between individuals in a population
- there is a struggle for existence as usually there are more individuals than can survive
- the best adapted survive; this he called 'survival of the fittest'

- the best adapted survive to breed and pass their favourable characteristics on to their offspring.

Two examples of natural selection are shown in the boxes.

Antibiotic resistance in bacteria

- When treated with an antibiotic some bacteria may be resistant (due to a mutation).
- These bacteria survive as the rest are killed.
- The resistant bacteria survive to breed and soon become the dominant type in the population.

The peppered moth

The peppered moth exists in two forms: light coloured and black.
In non-polluted areas the light form is well camouflaged on the bark of trees whereas the black form is easily spotted and eaten by birds. In these areas the light forms are most common.
In industrial areas where the trees are black with pollution the black forms are better adapted and survive better and increase in number.

Question

1 In a typical pasture there may be a few plants that have a gene resistant to high levels of copper in the soil. In these conditions the normal grasses grow better than the copper-resistant variety. However, in areas where the soil is contaminated with copper the copper-resistant variety may make up over 90% of the plants present. Explain this observation. *[4]*

Typical answer

1 The following four points for 4 marks.

- *In copper-contaminated areas the resistant gene is an advantage.* *[1]*
- *Copper-resistant plants are more likely to survive/fitter/better adapted.* *[1]*
- *Copper-resistant plants are more likely to have offspring/pass genes on to next generation.* *[1]*
- *% copper-resistant genes increases over time in the population.* *[1]*

Artificial selection

Plants and animals with desired characteristics can be selected and mated to produce offspring with particular characteristics. This may involve many breeding cycles to ensure that the desired genes are present. Examples of characteristics selected for are increased yield, food value, hardiness and disease resistance.

Cereal crops provide good examples. Wheat has been artificially bred to produce plants that are consistently short and of similar length (to reduce wind damage and ease harvesting) and have large heads of grain (to increase yield).

Exam questions

1 The diagram shows the variation in height of a group of men.

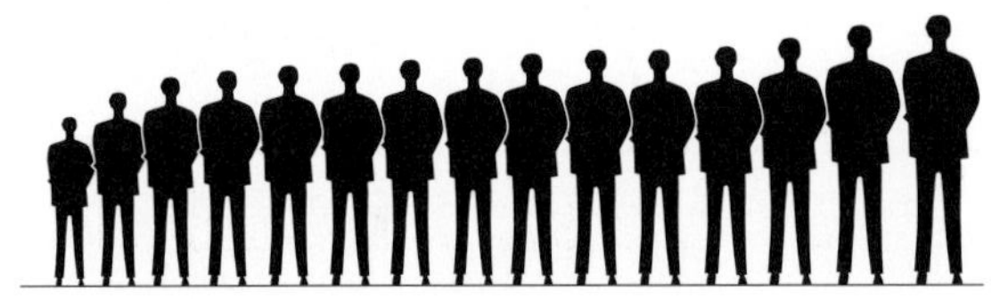

a Name the type of variation shown by the height of the group. *[1]*

The factors which cause such variation are genetic and environmental.

b i What is a genetic factor? *[1]*

Food is an environmental factor.

ii Suggest how food may cause variation in height. *[2]*

Tongue rolling is a characteristic which shows a different type of variation.

c Name this type of variation and explain how it differs from that shown by height. *[2]*

Biology Paper 1 Higher
June 2005

2 a Man can produce clones in animals. One method is by the splitting of early embryos in cows. The diagram shows the process.

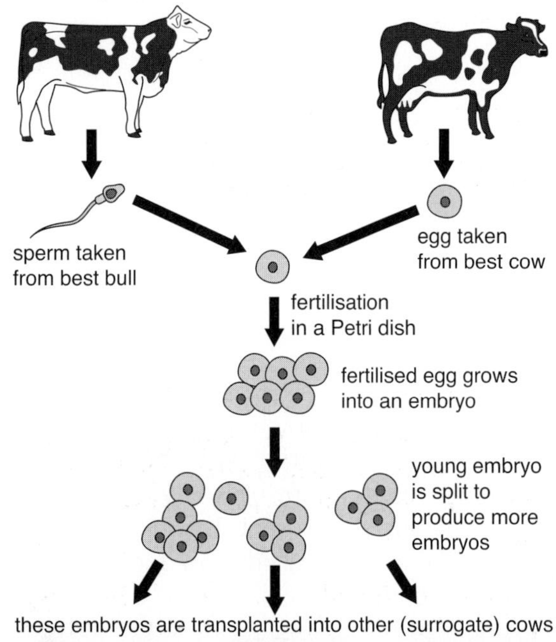
sperm taken from best bull
egg taken from best cow
fertilisation in a Petri dish
fertilised egg grows into an embryo
young embryo is split to produce more embryos
these embryos are transplanted into other (surrogate) cows

Use the information in the diagram and your knowledge to answer the following questions.

i Explain why this process results in **identical** offspring. *[1]*

ii What is the advantage, to the farmer, of producing calves using this method? *[1]*

b Part of Darwin's Theory of Natural Selection states that those organisms that are most suited to their environment are the most likely to survive. The diagram shows two forms of the peppered moth: the pale form and the dark form.

Peppered moths rest on tree trunks during the day. They are predated upon by birds. Before the Industrial Revolution in the 1800s, there was little soot in the air and tree trunks were pale coloured. The pale form of the peppered moth was the most common form.
Use the information in the diagram, the passage, and your knowledge to explain why by 1895, almost the entire population of moths in **industrialised** cities was the **dark** form. *[4]*

c The diagram shows two types of apple, a crab apple and a cultivated apple. The cultivated apple is the result of **artificial** selection.

crab apple

cultivated apple

i What is artificial selection? *[1]*

ii Use the diagram and your knowledge to suggest **two** characteristics that may have been artificially selected in the cultivated apple. *[2]*

Double Award (Modular) Paper 1 Higher
June 2006

18

Plant reproduction

The **flower** is the organ of reproduction in plants. Most flowers have the same general structure as in Figure 18.1. As in sexual reproduction in any organism, the flower produces gametes that produce new individuals during the process of fertilisation.

Figure 18.1 The general structure of a flower

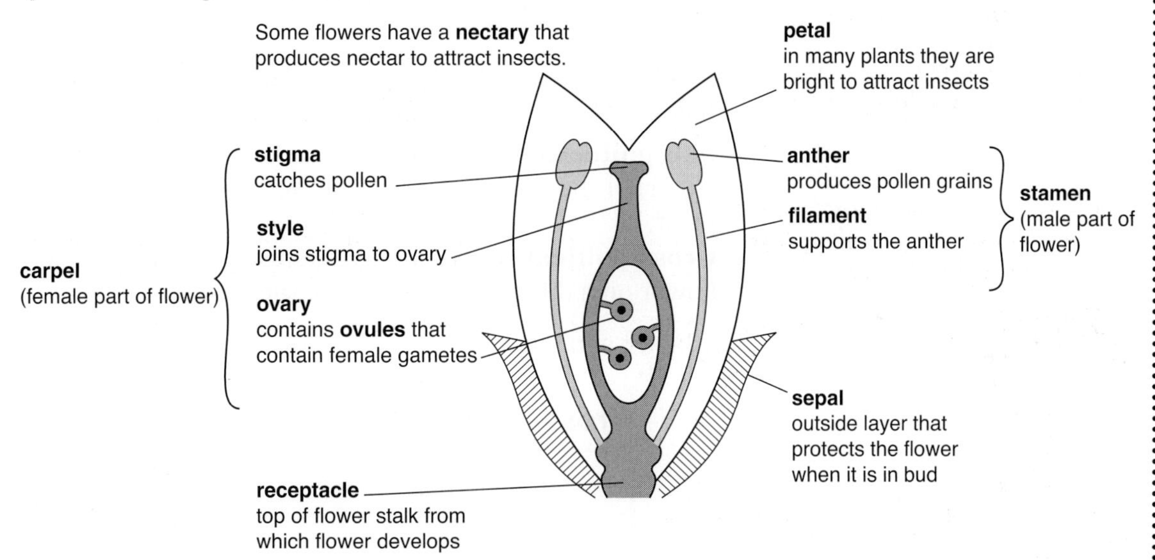

Some flowers have a **nectary** that produces nectar to attract insects.
petal
in many plants they are bright to attract insects
stigma
catches pollen
style
joins stigma to ovary
carpel
(female part of flower)
ovary
contains **ovules** that contain female gametes
anther
produces pollen grains
filament
supports the anther
stamen
(male part of flower)
sepal
outside layer that protects the flower when it is in bud
receptacle
top of flower stalk from which flower develops

The reproductive process

There are two distinct phases in plant reproduction:

- **pollination:** transfer of pollen from an anther to a stigma
- **fertilisation:** occurs when the male gamete (pollen grain nucleus) fuses with the female gamete (the ovule nucleus) in an ovule.

Pollination may be either by **insect** or by **wind**. Depending on which type of pollination is involved the flowers (and pollen) are adapted accordingly as shown in Table 18.1.

Table 18.1 Adaptations of insect-pollinated and wind-pollinated flowers

Insect-pollinated flowers	Wind-pollinated flowers
large bright petals to attract insects	petals usually small and not coloured
anthers and stigmas positioned inside the flower to make contact with insects feeding inside the flower	anthers and stigmas large and hanging outside the flower to catch the wind and pollen respectively
nectary frequently present	nectary absent
may produce scent	no scent produced
few large sticky pollen grains produced to stick to insects	large numbers of small pollen grains produced; large numbers needed as many are wasted and light as more easily carried by the wind

Self-pollination and cross-pollination

The differences in self-pollination and cross-pollination are as follows.

- **Self-pollination:** pollen transferred from an anther to a stigma of the same flower or another flower on the same plant.
- **Cross-pollination:** pollen transferred to a stigma of a flower on a different plant (of the same species).

The boxes summarise the two processes.

Self-pollination

- more reliable due to short distance involved
- disadvantage is that one parent only is involved and therefore it does not produce genetic variation

Cross-pollination

- less reliable but big advantage is that genetic variation is produced as two parents are involved
- cross-pollination is ensured or encouraged by:
  - separate sexed flowers, for example holly
  - male and female parts maturing at different times on same plant, for example wild garlic
  - stigmas raised in position above the anthers, for example daffodil

Pollination and fertilisation

The processes of pollination and fertilisation are closely linked in plants as shown in Figure 18.2.

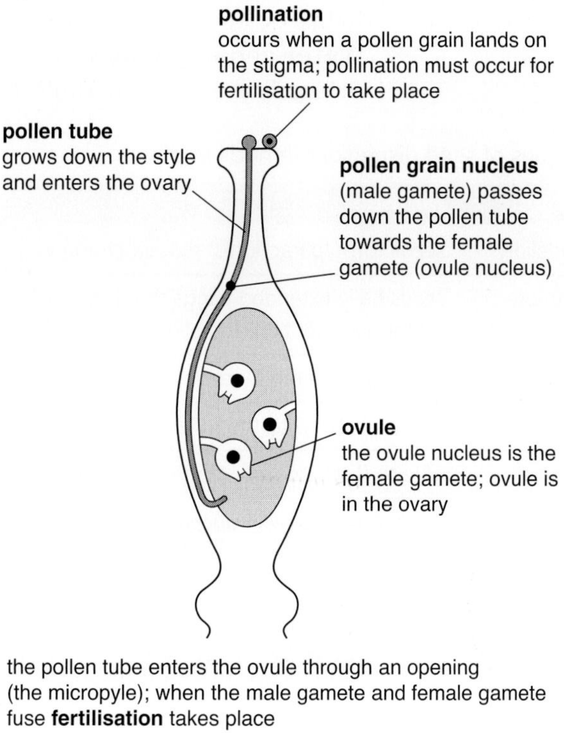

pollination
occurs when a pollen grain lands on the stigma; pollination must occur for fertilisation to take place

pollen tube
grows down the style and enters the ovary

pollen grain nucleus
(male gamete) passes down the pollen tube towards the female gamete (ovule nucleus)

ovule
the ovule nucleus is the female gamete; ovule is in the ovary

the pollen tube enters the ovule through an opening (the micropyle); when the male gamete and female gamete fuse **fertilisation** takes place

Figure 18.2 The processes of pollination and fertilisation in a plant

Question

1 a Explain why fertilisation cannot occur without pollination. *[1]*

b Suggest **one** reason why it is possible for a pollen grain to land on the stigma (pollination) but for its nucleus not to fertilise an ovule nucleus. *[1]*

c If the diploid number of chromosomes in a plant is 20, how many chromosomes will be in:

i a cell in the ovary wall

ii a cell in the coat of a pollen grain

iii the ovule nucleus? *[3]*

Typical answer

1 a The pollen grain must land on the stigma before the events leading to fertilisation can occur. *[1]*

b All ovules already fertilised/the grain does not develop a pollen tube/the tube stops growing. *[1]*

c i 20; **ii** 20; **iii** 10. *[3]*

Seed and fruit dispersal

Following fertilisation the ovule develops into a **seed** and the ovary becomes the **fruit**. These are then scattered away from the parent plant to avoid competition and to reach new habitats. Methods of dispersal include **wind**, **animals**, **water** and **explosive** mechanisms. Examples of the methods are given in Table 18.2.

Table 18.2 Examples of seed dispersal methods in plants

Type	Example	Method
wind	dandelion	seeds form 'parachutes' that catch the wind
wind	sycamore	seeds have extended wings that have 'helicopter' effect keeping the seed in the air for a longer time to catch the wind
animal	blackberry	juicy fruit is eaten by birds and the seeds dropped later
animal	goosegrass	sticky to attach to the fur of animals or clothes of humans
water	coconut	able to float around island edges and between islands
explosive	pea	as fruit (pod) dries it uncoils rapidly to eject seed

Seed structure

The structure of a bean seed is shown in Figure 18.3.

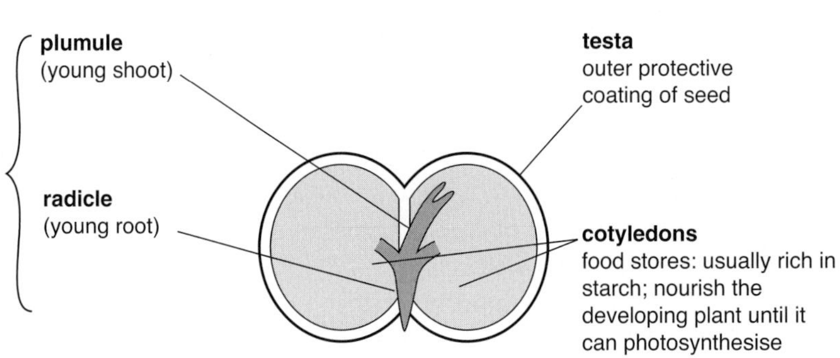
start to grow as seed germinates
plumule
(young shoot)
radicle
(young root)
testa
outer protective coating of seed
cotyledons
food stores: usually rich in starch; nourish the developing plant until it can photosynthesise

Figure 18.3 Bean seed (split to show the internal structure)

Some seeds have an additional food store called an **endosperm**.

Natural and artificial propagation

Many plants can reproduce without involving flowers. This is called asexual reproduction or propagation.

- **Natural propagation:** examples are strawberry runners and daughter bulbs in daffodils.
- **Artificial propagation:** examples are taking cuttings.

Exam question

1 a The diagram shows a buttercup flower.

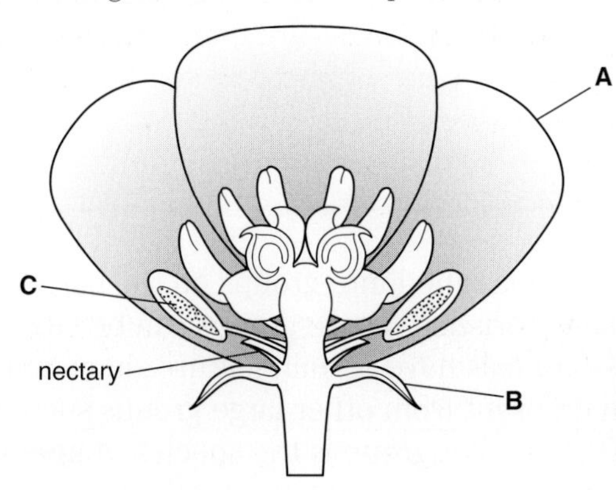
A
C
nectary
B

i Name parts A and B. *[2]*

ii Give the function of parts B and C. *[2]*

The buttercup is pollinated by insects.

iii Give **two** structures, shown in the diagram, which are adaptations to this method of pollination. *[2]*

iv Explain cross-pollination. *[2]*

The diagram shows flowers of a grass.

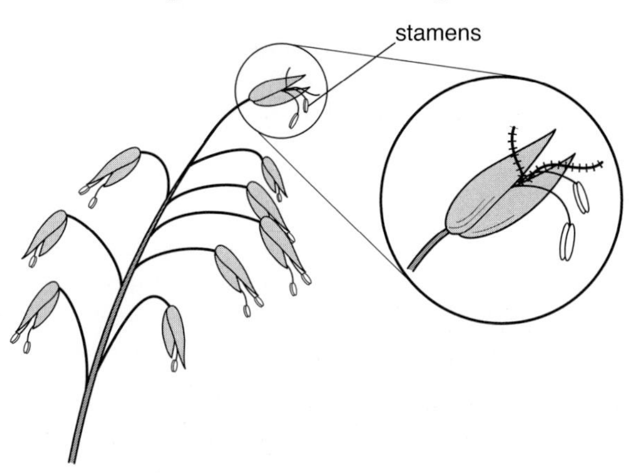
stamens

v Explain how the stamens are adapted for pollination. *[2]*

b The diagram shows different types of fruit.

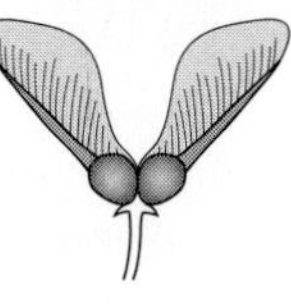
sycamore

wallflower

strawberry

i Name the fruit whose seed is dispersed by wind. Explain your answer. *[3]*

When strawberries are eaten by birds the seeds are dropped in their faeces.

ii Suggest why the bird is attracted to the strawberry as food. *[1]*

iii Explain why the seeds can still germinate after passing through the intestine of the bird. *[1]*

iv Give **one** reason why seed dispersal is necessary. *[1]*

c The diagram shows a section of a seed.

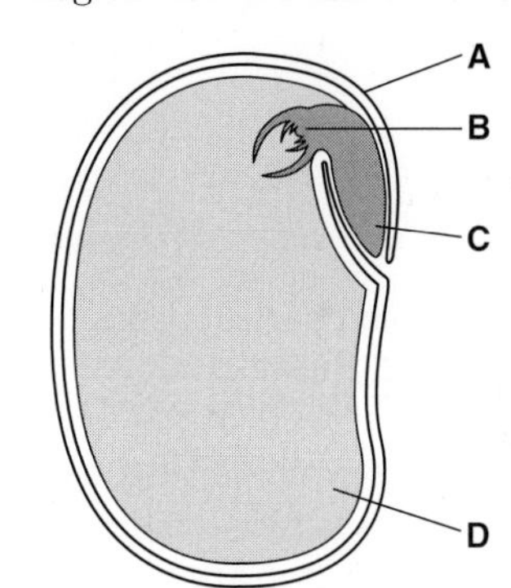
A
B
C
D

i Name parts **A**, **B** and **C**. *[3]*

ii Give the function of **D**. *[1]*

d Explain how runners increase the number of strawberry plants. *[2]*

Biology Paper 2 Foundation June 2006

19

Classification

Living organisms are classified into groups on the basis of having similar characteristics. These groups can be large, for example animals (animals have certain features in common that makes them different from other large groups such as plants and fungi). A smaller group is the species. A **species** is a group of organisms that resemble each other and can breed together to produce fertile young.

The major groups are the **plants**, **animals** and **fungi**.

Plants

Plants are all multi-cellular organisms that have cellulose cell walls that contain chlorophyll and produce food by photosynthesis. The main characteristics of plants are shown in Table 19.1.

Table 19.1 The main characteristics of plant groups

Plant group	Main characteristics	Examples/notes
algae	do not have roots, stems, leaves or vascular tissue (xylem and phloem)	green filamentous algae – found floating in water in filaments which contain groups of identical cells; brown seaweeds – look more differentiated but do not have true roots etc. – example is bladder wrack **Note:** it is brown because different pigments are used to trap light
bryophytes (mosses)	have stems and leaves but not vascular tissue or true roots (root-like structures called rhizoids are for attachment only); produce spores from tall capsules that arise out of the plant	found in damp areas as no roots to absorb water; do not grow tall as no vascular tissue to provide support
pteridophytes (ferns)	have roots, stems, leaves and vascular tissue; produce spores on underside of leaf	bracken; can grow much taller than mosses due to the presence of vascular tissue; live in drier areas as have true roots to absorb water
spermatophytes (angiosperms)	have roots, stems, leaves and vascular tissue; reproduce by flowers that produce seeds	daffodil

Animals

Animals are all multi-cellular organisms that feed on organic matter. They do not have cellulose and most are mobile.

There are two main sub-divisions:

- **invertebrates:** animals without backbones, for example annelids, arthropods and molluscs
- **vertebrates:** animals with backbones, for example chordates.

All the invertebrate groups have a variable body temperature in contrast to the chordates where only birds and mammals have a constant body temperature. The main characteristics of these groups are shown in Table 19.2.

Table 19.2 The main characteristics of invertebrates and chordates (vertebrates)

Animal group	Main characteristics	Examples/notes
annelids	formed of segments (segmentation); have small spikes on the lower surface (chaetae) that allow them to attach to the ground	earthworm
arthropods (insects)	have an exoskeleton, body in three parts (head, thorax, abdomen), three pairs of jointed legs and two pairs of wings	locust
molluscs	exoskeleton is in the form of a shell	snails and bivalves
chordates	animals with backbones (vertebrates)	chordates are sub-divided into groups of bony fish; reptiles; mammals; amphibians; birds

The following boxes summarise the features of the chordate sub-groups.

Bony fish

- Have gills, fins, scales.
- Body temperature not constant.
- Large number of eggs produced as external fertilisation.
- Example herring.

Reptiles

- Scales.
- Body temperature not constant.
- Internal fertilisation with small number of eggs laid on land.
- Parental care.
- Example crocodile.

Mammals

- Mammary glands; hair; ear pinna.
- Constant body temperature.
- Internal fertilisation and development.
- Parental care.
- Example man.

Birds

- Feathers; wings; beak.
- Constant body temperature.
- Small number of shelled eggs cared for by parent.
- Example thrush.

Amphibians

- Moist skin; lungs in adults.
- Body temperature not constant. External fertilisation producing many eggs.
- Example of young is tadpole; adult is frog.

Plant and animal adaptations

Plants and animals show adaptations to suit the environment in which they live.

Life in water

An example is fish. They have:

- a streamlined shape
- fins for stability and movement
- gills for gas exchange.

Life on land

An example is angiosperms (flowering plants). They have:

- roots to obtain water
- vascular tissue for support and water transport
- seeds that are resistant to water loss
- a cuticle to reduce water loss from leaves.

Another example is mammals. They have:

- a thick skin to reduce moisture loss
- internal fertilisation (external fertilisation can only occur in water)
- a skeleton for support and movement.

Even within closely related species plants or animals can be adapted for very different environments.

- **Arctic fox:** has small ears to reduce heat loss and thick white fur for insulation and camouflage.
- **Desert fox:** has large ears to encourage heat loss by radiation and thin brown fur to encourage heat loss and for camouflage.

Fungi

Note: Although fungi are plant-like they are classified as a separate group from plants.

The main adaptations of fungi are shown in Figure 19.1.

Figure 19.1
The adaptations in fungi

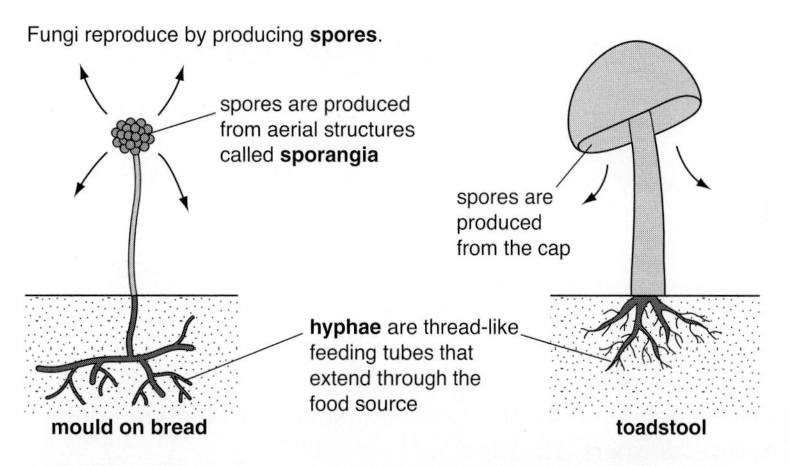
Fungi reproduce by producing **spores**.
spores are produced from aerial structures called **sporangia**
spores are produced from the cap
hyphae are thread-like feeding tubes that extend through the food source
mould on bread
toadstool

Fungi do not have chlorophyll. They feed **saprophytically** by releasing enzymes in the hyphae into the food source (substrate). The enzymes break down the food in **extracellular** (outside the cell) **digestion** and the nutrients are then absorbed.

Exam questions

1 The diagram shows three invertebrates.

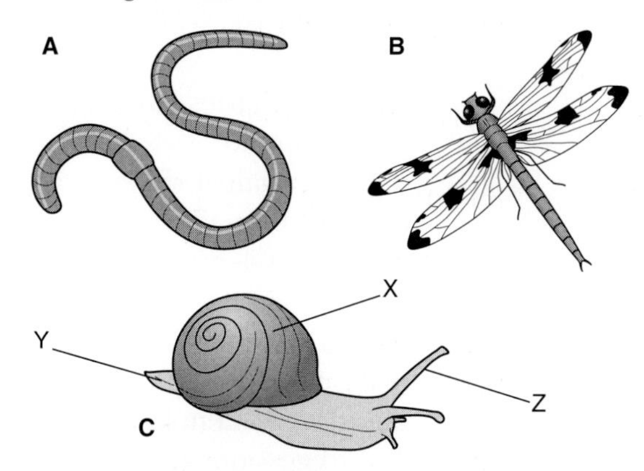
A
B
C
X
Y
Z

a Give **one** feature, not shown in the diagram, which invertebrates have in common. *[1]*

b i Which organism, **A**, **B** or **C**, is an insect? *[1]*

ii Give one feature of insects. *[1]*

c Which organism, **A**, **B** or **C**, has chaetae? *[1]*

d i Give the label (**X**, **Y** or **Z**) on organism **C** that shows the exoskeleton. *[1]*

ii Name the group to which organism **C** belongs. *[1]*

Biology Paper 1 Foundation June 2006

2 The diagram shows a fish and a mammal.

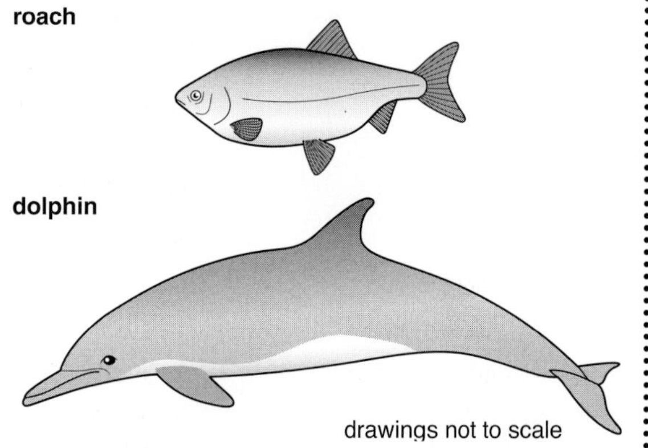
roach
dolphin
drawings not to scale

a i Give **one** feature, shown in both animals, which adapts them for life in water. **Explain** how the feature helps them to live in water. *[2]*

ii Give **one** difference between the animals. *[1]*

iii Name the animal group to which a dolphin belongs. *[1]*

iv Give **two** features of the animal group to which a dolphin belongs. *[2]*

Biology Paper 2 Foundation June 2006

Index